ASHTANGA YOGA
PRIMER

ASHTANGA YOCA PI

RIMER

Baba Hari Dass

SRI
RAMA

Photography by
  Steven N. Thomas (Mukund)
        Illustrations by Satyawan Steven Jones

SRI RAMA PUBLISHING / HANUMAN FELLOWSHIP
Santa Cruz, California

*"Don't think that you
are carrying
the whole world;
make it easy,
make it play,
make it a prayer."*

Design, calligraphy, and production by Josh Gitomer
Edited and typeset by Karuna Ault
First printing, 1981
10   9   8   7
ISBN: 978-0-918100-04-7
Library of Congress Catalog Card No. 81-51052

SRI RAMA PUBLISHING is a non-profit organization founded
to produce the writings of Baba Hari Dass.
Profits from the sale of books
and recordings are used to support our orphanage
in northern India. (see page 75)

TABLE *of* CONTENTS

> "Kundalini *is the greatest energy in the human body. If* kundalini *is awakened it entirely changes the person, who then dwells in complete peace and clarity of mind.*"

ASHTANGA YOGA THEORY

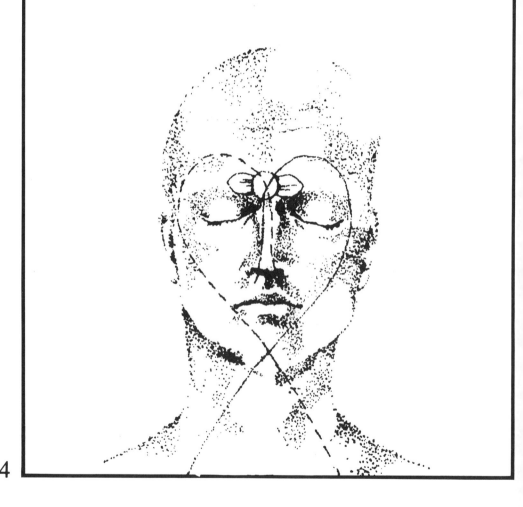

INTRODUCTION

THE ANCIENT* SAGE PATANJALI was the first to systematize the practices of Ashtanga Yoga. The second verse of his famous *Yoga Sutras* defines Yoga thus:

Yogash Chitta Vritti Nirodhah
(Yoga is the cessation of thought-waves in the mind.)
YOGA SUTRAS 1:2

Yoga literally means "union". Through stilling the mind, union with our divine source is achieved.

Practices of Yoga *(sadhana)* purify the body and the mind for the purpose of developing concentration. Perfect concentration leads to a thoughtless mind and superconsciousness *(samadhi)*. This higher consciousness brings knowledge of reality and peace.

Patanjali described this process as having eight parts or "limbs"; thus the system is called *Ashtanga (ashta* = eight,

anga = limb) *Yoga.* The eight limbs are: *yama* (restraints), *niyama* (observances), *asana* (posture, seat), *pranayama* (control of *prana,* breath), *pratyahara* (withdrawing the mind from sense perception), *dharana* (concentration), *dhyana* (meditation), and *samadhi* (superconsciousness).

THE EIGHT LIMBS

Yama
(Restraints)

Ahimsa (nonviolence), *satya* (truthfulness), *asteya* (non-stealing), *brahmacharya* (continence), & *aparigraha* (non-possessiveness) are the five restraints.
YOGA SUTRAS 2:30

Ahimsa (nonviolence): To refrain from causing pain to any living being, including oneself. Every action, word, or thought that causes pain to another—any thought containing anger, greed, lust, or attachment—is a form of violence. With perfection of *ahimsa,* one's nonviolent nature and peace radiate to others. Even violent creatures (e.g. wild

"The aim of life is to attain peace. No one can give us peace. We can't buy or borrow it. We have to cultivate it by practicing yama *and* niyama.*"*

---

*Although Patanjali's exact dates are unknown, he wrote the *Yoga Sutras* some centuries before Christ.

5

*"Do your work
by surrendering to God.
Don't think that
you are helping others, but
think that God is
helping them,
taking you
as an instrument."*

animals) abandon their hostility in the presence of such a nonviolent being.

Satya (truthfulness): To develop honesty; to avoid deceiving others and oneself. Cultivating truthfulness requires the aspirant to avoid exaggeration, rationalization, pretense, and all other variants of deceit. When truthfulness is perfected, one's words and blessings always come true.

Asteya (non-stealing): To avoid any kind of misappropriation of material or non-material things, such as acceptance of undeserved praise. When non-stealing is perfected, one is freed from the illusion of ownership: me/mine, you/yours.

Brahmacharya (continence): To conserve and redirect the sexual energy. Literally translated, *brahmacharya* means "to walk on God's path". Perfect celibacy is, above all, an attitude of mind—purity of thought, word, and deed. To aid in the practice of celibacy one should eat sattvic food and avoid worldly situations and environments. When continence is perfected, one gains physical, mental, and spiritual strength.

Aparigraha (non-hoarding): To avoid the accumulation of unnecessary possessions. Its purpose is to become free not from possessions themselves, but from attachment to them so that one is unaffected by their gain or loss. Perfection of *aparigraha* gives dispassion and one gains knowledge of the past, present, and future.

6

Niyama
(Observances)

Shaucha (purity), *santosha* (contentment), *tapas* (austerity), *svadhyaya* (scriptural study), and *Ishvarapranidhana* (surrender to God) constitute observances.
YOGA SUTRAS 2:32

Shaucha (purity): Cleanliness of the body and purity of the mind. As the mind and body are interdependent, purification of the body is a means of controlling the mind. External cleanliness on the gross level includes daily bathing, wearing clean clothes, living in a clean house; on the subtle level it is purity of action or selfless service. Internal cleanliness on the gross level includes the system of *shat karma* (six purificatory techniques—see page 15); on the subtle level it is the eradication of negative qualities and thoughts from the mind.

By observing cleanliness one becomes less attached to one's own body, and loses desire for physical contact with others. When purity is perfected, one gains control of the senses and becomes cheerful, one-pointed, and fit for Self-realization.

Santosha (contentment): More than a passive state of mind, contentment is a virtue to be actively cultivated in order to free the mind from the effects of pleasure and pain. When contentment is perfected, one becomes desireless and attains unexcelled happiness.

austerity—extremely self-disciplined

Tapas (austerity): Literally, "to burn"; in Yoga *tapas* implies the burning of all desires by means of discipline, purification, and penance. Fasting, enduring heat or cold, and observing silence are methods of *tapas.* Any form of giving up desires is *tapas. Pranayama* (breath control) is considered to be the highest austerity, as it requires great restraint of the normal, life-giving breath. When austerity is perfected one achieves control over the body and the senses.

Svadhyaya (scriptural study): The study of scriptures, Self-inquiry, *satsang,* and *japa* (repetition) of *Om,* with the aim of attaining liberation.

Study of scriptures pertains especially to the Vedas; it also includes study of the lives and teachings of saints. Self-inquiry is done by reflecting deeply on the question, "Who am I?" *Satsang* is association with spiritually oriented people and places. As *Om* is the origin of all *mantras* (sacred sounds or words), *japa* of *Om* may be extended to include any *mantra* used for liberation. Through *svadhyaya* one can contact the form of God that one desires to worship.

Ishvarapranidhana (surrender to God): Recognition that the limited, ego-self is an illusion; channeling of energies toward the realization of truth, or God. One who sees the Self in all beings and who has surrendered the ego of being the "doer" is the true practitioner of *Ishvarapranidhana.* Perfection of *Ishvarapranidhana* brings success in *samadhi* (superconsciousness).

Asana
(Posture, Seat)

The word *asana* is commonly translated as "posture", but its literal meaning is "seat", referring particularly to meditation postures, which promote concentration of the mind. Since a healthy body is important for meditation, ancient yogis devised many different postures* to make the body strong, sound, and flexible.

Asanas help to balance the physical body by regulating glandular secretions, toning muscles and nerves, massaging internal organs, and improving circulation and digestion. Although *asanas* are not intended to build large muscles, they do make the body strong, flexible, & proportionate; thin bodies are developed, while unnecessary fat is reduced. *Asanas* increase endurance, will power, and resistance to disease. Through regular practice the mind becomes calm and undesireable thoughts gradually diminish.

Primarily, however, *asanas* function as a stimulant to the subtle body. They purify the subtle energy channels *(nadis)* and strengthen all five vital energies *(pranas).* They direct the flow of *prana* upward, aiding in the awakening of *kundalini,* the great reservoir of spiritual energy situated at the base of the spine.

---

*These are actually part of the system of Hatha Yoga.

"No one can have everything. You have to be content with what you have and what you get. Running to get everything is like a deer who runs after a mirage and dies with thirst."

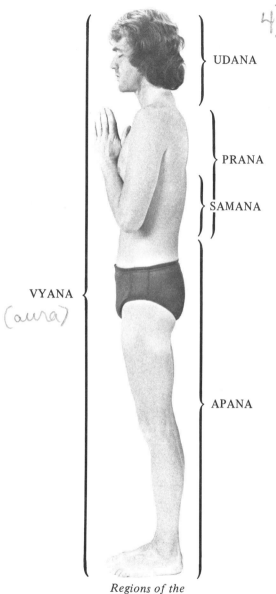

UDANA

PRANA

SAMANA

VYANA
(aura)

APANA

Regions of the five vayus

4) *Pranayama*
(Breath Control)

The fourth limb of Ashtanga Yoga is *pranayama.* The word *pranayama* is made of two words: *prana,* "vital energy"—that which makes all life and all physical activity possible; and *ayama,* "expansion". *Pranayama* is a method of breathing through which life-supporting energy is expanded.

Yoga (union) is achieved by stopping thought waves *(vrittis)* in the mind. Mental activity is correlated to breath; the more breaths there are, the more thoughts rush through the mind. The practice of *pranayama,* which involves a series of breathing exercises, drastically reduces the number of breaths taken in a given period. By calming the mind, it thus prepares one for concentration and meditation.

The practices of *pranayama* are based on the normal breathing pattern, which has four stages: inhalation, retention, exhalation, retention. *Pranayama* alters the ratio of these four parts; it is designed to slow down the rate of breathing and, especially, to lengthen breath retention *(kumbhaka).*

VAYUS
(Vital Airs)

The *vayus* are five specific manifestations of *prana* in the subtle body, each having a certain function and location in the physical body.

In the heart region
resides *prana vayu,*
in the anus region *apana vayu,*
in the navel region *samana vayu,*
in the throat region *udana vayu,*
and in the whole body
vyana vayu prevails.
GORAKSHA SAMHITA, verse 30

Udana vayu (rising air) functions between the throat and the top of the head; its normal movement is upward. It controls speech, vomiting, and balance, keeps the body upright, and gives strength to the memory and intellect. In Yoga *sadhana,* it carries *kundalini* to *sahasrara chakra.*

Prana vayu (vital air) functions between the throat and the navel. It controls respiration, speech, swallowing, circulation, body temperature, and perspiration. In Yoga it raises *kundalini* to *udana vayu.*

Samana vayu (unchanging air) functions between the navel and the heart, maintaining *apana* and *prana vayus* in a balanced state. It controls digestion, regulates digestive secretions in the stomach, liver, duodenum, and small intestines. This *vayu* distributes the essential parts of food, thereby nourishing the various parts of the body. In Yoga it stimulates *apana* and *prana vayus* and pushes *kundalini* upward.

Vyana vayu (diffused air) functions throughout the entire body, helping all other *pranas* to function. It controls body movement, circulation, heartbeat, and aids the function of the gross nerves and the subtle *nadis*. *Vyana vayu* appears as the *aura* around the body.

Apana vayu (downward air) functions from the navel to the soles of the feet; its normal movement is downward. It controls digestion, excretion, reproduction, and child delivery. In Yoga it carries *kundalini* upward in *sushumna* to unite with *prana vayu*.

Pratyahara
(Withdrawing the Mind from Sense Perception)

Pratyahara is the liberation of the senses from the objects that attract them. The word means "reversal" or "withdrawal"; it indicates that the normal outward flow of the senses must be reversed so that the senses can return to their origin in the mind.

The first four limbs of Ashtanga Yoga are external methods, the last three limbs are internal processes, and the fifth limb, *pratyahara*, is the bridge between the external and internal practices.

Normally the mind wanders involuntarily from the mental image of one sense object to another, and a desire is created. This desire pulls the mind outward. Awareness of this process is the beginning stage of *pratyahara*. By the practice of *yama, niyama, asana,* and *pranayama* the mind gradually withdraws from outer objects, turns inward, and concentrates on the Self. The senses follow the mind, withdrawing from the objects that attract them, and turn inward. Then the mind can go easily into *dharana, dhyana,* and *samadhi*.

Pratyahara is practiced by repeatedly pulling the mind back from going outward. Various methods are useful to help in *pratyahara: mantra* (the uttering of sacred sounds), *nada* (listening to inner sounds), *japa* (repetition of *mantra* or a name of God), *puja* (worship), *trataka* (gazing), *kirtana* (chanting), *mudra* (literally "seal", "lock"), and *nyasa* (projecting the divine principle onto various parts of the body). Two additional practices of *pratyahara* which are explained in detail in this book are *arati* (worship by light), page 56, and hand *mudras*, page 60.

Dharana (Concentration)

After the mind has been collected into itself, that is, when *pratyahara* has been accomplished, it must be directed toward one object of concentration. This focusing of attention onto one point is *dharana*, the sixth limb of Ashtanga Yoga.

The word *dharana* is derived from the root *dhā*, meaning "to hold, carry, support". It refers to the holding of an object in the mind. In *dharana* the mind dwells only on the chosen object, and is not allowed to wander to other objects.

Important objects of concentration are sixteen points within the body *(shodhashadhara)*: thumb, ankles, knees, thighs, foreskin, genitals, navel, heart, neck, throat, palate, nose, middle of

"All sadhanas or methods are for simply tricking the mind. The trick is to not let the mind spread out in a form of thoughts."

9

fire

water

earth

Six chakras and
sushumna nadi

Blaine
Lemert

the eyebrows, forehead, head, and *Brahmarandhra.**

Other suitable objects of concentration may be a picture of a deity, a *chakra,* one's breath, a visualization, a candle flame, or a *mantra.*

7) *Dhyana* (Meditation)

The word *dhyana* is derived from the root *dhi,* meaning "intellect". Meditation involves the channelling of intellect, or mind, to one point. *Dhyana* is a continuous succession of identical thoughts directed toward one object which happens so quickly that before one subsides another (same thought) takes its place.

Dhyana is distinguished from *dharana* (concentration) only by its uninterrupted nature. In scriptures the difference between concentration and meditation is described as the difference between pouring water and pouring oil: both streams fall toward one place, but water falls in a "broken" stream of drops whereas the stream of oil is smooth, constant, unbroken.

8) *Samadhi*
(Superconsciousness)

Samadhi is the final limb of Ashtanga Yoga. The word is derived from *sam* (together) + *ā* (completely) + *dhā* (to hold); thus "to hold together com-

10

pletely". *Samadhi* differs from *dhyana* in that there is no succession of identical thought waves, but rather complete identity or absorption in one object (thought).

Just as concentration culminates in meditation, so meditation culminates in *samadhi.* In meditation there is consciousness of mind and object only. When meditation becomes intense, the mind and object merge, and the mind is no longer conscious of itself. This dissolution of the subject-object relationship is *samadhi,* or, more correctly, the first stage of *samadhi.* The term *samadhi* actually refers to several stages of higher consciousness that become progressively more profound, finally culminating in *kaivalya*—perfect Self-realization. The stages of *samadhi* reflect the progressive withdrawal of consciousness into its source, the Self.

---

*lit. "hole of God", another name for mula.

THE
SUBTLE BODY

Within the physical body every human being has a subtle body made up of invisible structures and energies *(kundalini, nadis,* and *chakras);* and within the subtle body is the causal body out of which the subtle and physical bodies are formed. The subtle body can be understood as a bridge between the physical body and the causal body, and as the means by which the aspirant attains enlightenment. To derive the greatest benefit from the practices of Yoga, it is useful to learn something of the structures and processes of the subtle body.

Kundalini

Kundalini is a reservoir of energy *(prana)* stored at the base of the spine. Because it is a spiraling power, *kundalini* is described as a serpent, coiled three and one-half times around *svayambhu lingam* (see figure). By doing *sadhana* (spiritual practices) this *kundalini* energy is activated; it then moves up the subtle spinal channel *(sushumna nadi)*, piercing the energy centers *(chakras)*. So long as the illusion of "I am this body" persists, *kundalini* power remains inherent but inactive. It awakens only when attachment to the body begins to dissipate, and then it becomes the energy by which Yoga (union) is achieved.

Nadis

Nadis are the subtle channels through which vital energy *(prana)* flows. Although there is a vast network of *nadis* spread throughout the body, Yoga practice is primarily concerned with three main *nadis: sushumna, ida,* and *pingala.*

Of these three *nadis, sushumna* is the most important.

SUSHUMNA NADI

Sushumna nadi, the channel through which *kundalini* flows, begins at the base of the spine *(muladhara chakra,* where *kundalini* lies dormant) and runs upward through the spinal column. When it reaches a spot at the base of the skull *(mastaka granthi* or head knot), it divides into two branches. The main branch travels forward through the head to pierce *ajna chakra* (between the eyebrows) before reaching *mula* at the top of the head. Yoga *sadhana* is concerned only with this branch. The other branch travels up the back of the skull and meets the main branch at *mula.* (See figure on page 13.)

IDA & PINGALA NADIS

Ida begins on the left side of *sushumna* and *pingala* on the right side at the base of the spine. These two *nadis* spiral outside of and around *sushumna,* crossing each other between each *chakra* and at *mastaka granthi* at the base of the skull, like the two snakes of the familiar caduceus. From *mastaka granthi, ida* travels up and around the right side of the head; *pingala* moves similarly around the left side. They cross again in the center of *ajna chakra;* then *ida* exits through the left nostril, *pingala*

Kundalini
coiled around
svayambhu lingam
in the base
of muladhara chakra

Sunita Alyson King

11

through the right. *Ida* is associated with the moon and female energy, *pingala* with the sun and male energy.

Chakras

Chakras are specific energy centers that are related to the various actions of *prana.* Each of these centers is circular with a central point of focused energy known as *bindu;* thence the name *chakra,* which means "wheel". The *chakras* lie horizontally within *sushumna nadi.*

The seven major *chakras,* from lowest to highest, are as follows: *Muladhara chakra,* with four red petals, is located at the base of the spine and relates to the earth element. *Kundalini* is coiled in the base of this *chakra.*

Svadhishthana chakra, with six bright red-orange petals, is located at the level of the genitals and relates to the water element.

Manipura chakra, with ten blue petals, is located at the level of the navel and relates to the fire element.

Anahata chakra, with twelve red-violet petals, is located at the level of the heart and relates to the air element.

Vishuddha chakra, with sixteen gray petals, is located at the base of the neck and relates to the ether element.

Ajna chakra, with two bright white petals, is located four fingers' width behind the eyebrow center. Whereas the lower five *chakras* are within *sushumna nadi, ajna chakra* is pierced by *sushumna* at its *bindu* (center), which is called *kuta.*

Sahasrara chakra, with one thousand bright white petals, is located at the crown of the head. Whereas the lower six *chakras* are extremely small, lying in a horizontal position within *sushumna, sahasrara chakra* is large, filling the top of the skull and pointing forward and downward. The center *(bindu)* of the underside of *sahasrara chakra* is named *shri;* the upper side of this center is *mula. Kundalini* must pass through *shri* in order to attain the highest stage of knowledge. *Shri* is like a one-way valve—once *kundalini* has passed this point it cannot descend again.

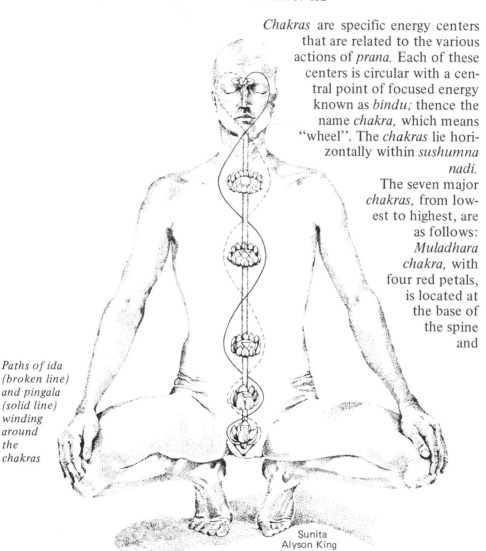

Paths of ida (broken line) and pingala (solid line) winding around the chakras

Sunita
Alyson King

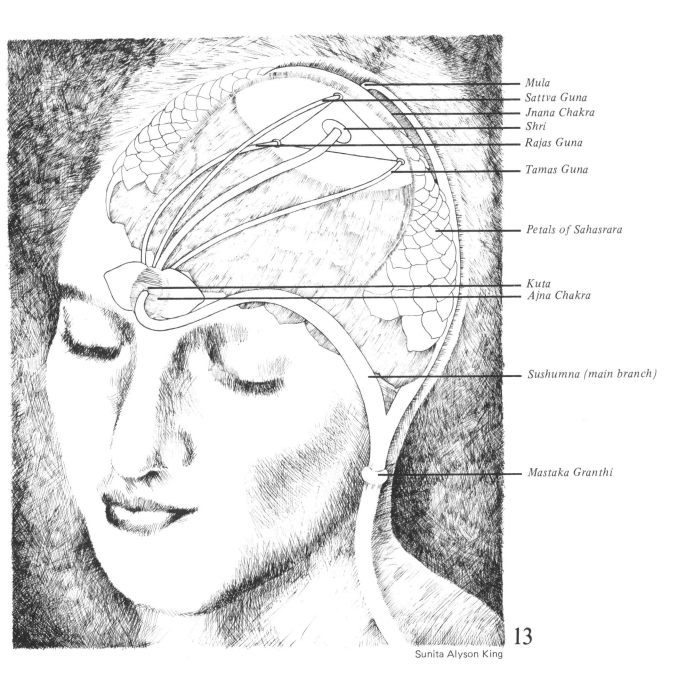

Mula
Sattva Guna
Jnana Chakra
Shri
Rajas Guna

Tamas Guna

Petals of Sahasrara

Kuta
Ajna Chakra

Sushumna (main branch)

Mastaka Granthi

13

Sunita Alyson King

"There is a hope of finding something. One doesn't proceed in darkness, but takes a lighted candle, which is sadhana. The more you step forward, the more the path appears in the light of that candle."

SADHANA (PRACTICE)

14

THE EFFORT TO ATTAIN PEACE by doing *sadhana* is called *abhyasah*, persistent practice. If one practices regularly for a long time with devotion and honest effort, one will attain success. 'Long time' cannot be exactly defined—it varies with each person.

Do your *sadhana* regularly; one hour each day is incomparably better than three hours every third day. It is also helpful to have a fixed hour and place for your practice.

You have to understand that there can't be a right practice without regular practice. Regular practice makes it 'right'. For example, meditation: meditating for a few days and then not meditating for several days is a wrong practice. If one meditates regularly at a regular time, then meditation will progress and one will learn how to meditate properly. Also, without faith, devotion, and right attitude one can't progress.

SHAT KARMA
(Six Purificatory Methods)

Yoga emphasizes a clean, healthy, and vibrant body, as the body is the vehicle by which higher consciousness is attained. So an aspirant practices the Six Purificatory Methods *(Shat Karma)* which remove toxins and impurities, increase the body's resistance to disease, and purify the *nadis* (subtle energy channels).

The six methods are: *neti* (nasal cleaning), *dhauti* (washing), *vasti* (enema), *trataka* (forehead wash, gazing), *nauli* (intestinal wash, lit. "churning"), and *kapala bhati* (skull shining).

Neti (Nasal Cleaning)

Neti opens the sinus passages and cleans out nasal mucus. It excites the *nadis* and aids in *pranayama*. There are two methods: *jala* (water) *neti* and *sutra* (string) *neti*.

JALA NETI
(Nasal Cleaning with Water)

A small pot with a spout that extends from the bottom of the pot is needed for this practice.* Fill the pot with tepid salt water (one teaspoon of salt to a pint of water). Open the mouth and breathe through it. Insert the spout into one nostril, tipping the head side-

---

*The spout of a small plastic watering pot can be cut to about four inches to make a suitable *jala neti* pot.

*Above: traditional
jala neti pot
Below: method of
jala neti*

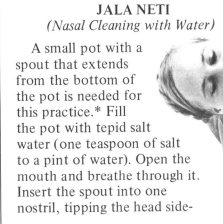

15

ways and slightly forward so the open nostril is lower than the water pot. If the head is tipped properly, the water will easily flow down and out of the lower nostril. Repeat method with other nostril. Blow the nose well afterward. Bending the head down to the knees helps release excess water. *Jala neti* can be done every day.

SUTRA NETI
(Nasal Cleaning with String)

This technique uses a specially prepared strip of cotton batiste, part of which (about six inches) is twisted tightly and coated smoothly with beeswax. The tail-ends, left uncoated, are about eight inches long. Wet the string; curve the tip of the waxed part and gently insert it into one nostril. Push it back until the tip of the string is visible in the throat. Then reach into the throat and, **very slowly,** pull the string out through the mouth. Repeat in the other nostril. This technique may be practiced daily. It is particularly beneficial in the case of deviated septum, using a thin string first and gradually increasing its thickness. **Caution**: If one has frequent nosebleeds, or lesions inside the nose, *sutra neti* is not advised.

Neti string and method of sutra neti

Dhauti (Washing)

There are various methods of *dhauti.* This manual includes only those which are practiced in the beginning and intermediate stages of *sadhana.* For some of the *dhauti* methods, the direct supervision of an experienced teacher is recommended.

DANTA DHAUTI
(Washing of the Teeth, Tongue, Ears, Eyes, & Forehead)

Teeth: Brush two or three times daily; use dental floss once daily.

Tongue: Rub the tongue with the three middle fingers. Push fingers back to the uvula; the gagging reflex will clear out all phlegm.

Ears: With wet finger clean the opening of the ears.

Eyes: Scoop clean water up in the palms and flush the eyes.

Forehead: Rub the indentation between the forehead and the nose with the thumb.

AGNISARA DHAUTI
(Washing by Fire)

See "Four Purifications", page 21.

VAMANA DHAUTI
(Washing by Vomiting)

On an empty stomach, drink one quart of tepid salt water (one teaspoon salt per pint of water). It is best to drink it all at once, rather than a little at a time. Bend forward and release the water by vomiting. If necessary one can tickle the back of the throat, which should bring the water up easily. After doing this practice, wait at least fifteen minutes before eating; avoid acidic or spicy foods. *Vamana dhauti* should be done no more than once a week.

Vamana dhauti cleans the upper digestive tract of excess acids and mucus, promoting good digestion.

VASTRA DHAUTI
(Washing with a Cloth)

This practice must not be attempted without the supervision of an experienced teacher. *Vastra dhauti* is done with a strip of cotton batiste, twenty-two feet long and three inches wide (before hemming). Turn the long edges over twice and hem them so that there are no loose threads. Roll the cloth like a bandage and boil it for several minutes to sterilize it. Then put one unhemmed end in the mouth and begin to swallow the cloth. It helps to drink sips of water, and to push the cloth to one side of the throat when swallowing.

Do not spend more than thirty minutes trying to swallow the cloth. Leave at least twelve inches of the cloth unswallowed in order to remove it.

When removing the cloth, one should try to relax as much as possible. Pull the cloth out gently and slowly. If it doesn't come out easily, take a drink of water, milk, or oil and again pull gently.

Vastra dhauti removes excess mucus and wastes from the stomach & throat. It clears the bronchials, the lungs, and is helpful in the treatment of asthma.

VARISARA DHAUTI
(Washing with Water)

Varisara dhauti is a method of washing the intestines with water. Another name for it is *shankhaprakshalana*. This practice cleans the intestines, improves digestion, purifies the *nadis,* and makes the body light. It should be learned from an experienced teacher.

—Eat light food the preceding day (if possible take only liquids after twelve noon), and take no food or drink in the morning before the practice.

—Begin early enough in the morning so that the method is completed before normal breakfast hour.

—Do not do *varisara dhauti* in cold weather.

—Do *varisara dhauti* no more often than once a month.

—*Varisara dhauti* should not be practiced by people with ulcers or high blood pressure.

Method

Prepare two or three gallons of lukewarm, salted water (one teaspoon salt per pint of water). In a squatting position, drink one quart of the water. Then do the following *asanas:*

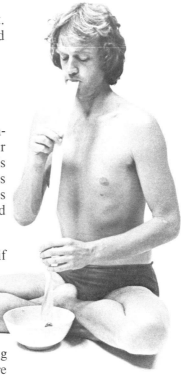

Method of vastra dhauti

17

Twisting Cobra Pose
(Tiryaka Bhujangasana)

Lie on the stomach with palms flat on floor beside shoulders. Push torso off the floor with hands, twist head to the right and look back at heels; then twist to the left and look back. Do this four times.

Palm Tree Pose
(Urdhva Hastottanasana)

Stand and do this Palm Tree variation, clasping hands above the head and twisting upper body from side to side four times.

Waist Rotation
(Kati Chakrasana)

Stand with feet comfortably apart and arms outstretched to either side. Twist torso to the right and then to the left. Do this four times.

Stomach-Squeezing Pose
(Udarakarshanasana)

Squat with feet apart and hands on knees. Shift the body's weight to ball of left foot (by sitting on left heel) and at the same time bring left knee to meet right ankle (knee does not touch floor); twist upper body to the right and look back over right shoulder. (Be sure to keep weight on the left foot.) Then shift weight to the right foot and reverse. Do four times.

Drink another quart of water and repeat the *asana* series, and again drink water and do the *asanas*. Then go to the toilet. **Do not use force.** Now repeat the sequence drinking only one pint of water each time: water, *asanas*, toilet—until clear water is released through the anus. Then stop. Lie down and rest for forty-five minutes to one hour. After resting it is necessary to eat some light, simple food that is not pungent, acidic, or cold (e.g. porridge, rice pudding, soup). Eat butter or ghee with the food to lubricate the intestines. (Do not let more than one hour elapse before eating.) After eating, rest again for several hours.

Vasti *(Enema)*

There are several methods of *vasti*, some cleaning with air and some with water. The simplest method is a type of *jala vasti* (water enema), for which a small tube is needed. The tube should be about six inches long and one-half inch in diameter. (A piece of smooth bamboo or rubber catheter will work well.) Mark the middle of the tube by tying a piece of tape or string around it. Rub vaseline on one end of the tube, and gently insert it about three inches into the rectum. Squat in a tub of tepid water, navel deep. Lift and release the intestines several times, or do *nauli*, and water will rush inside the large intestine. Remove the tube and expel the water in an appropriate place.

A person who tends to be constipated can practice *vasti* twice a week, one with normal bowels once a week, and one with loose bowels twice a month. *Vasti* should not be practiced in the case of fever, ulcers, or hemorrhoids. *Vasti* alleviates urinary problems, digestive disorders, and flatulence.

Trataka (*Forehead Wash, Gazing*)

Trataka is gazing at one object without blinking. This strengthens & cleans the eyes. *Trataka* also purifies the mind, and can be used as a practice of *pratyahara, dharana,* or *dhyana.* Suitable objects for *trataka* include: a black or bright-colored dot drawn on a piece of paper and fixed on a wall at eye level, a candle flame placed several feet away at eye level, the horizon, the full moon, a treetop silhouetted against the sky, the tip of the nose, a point three to four inches beyond the tip of the nose, or the eyebrow center (*ajna chakra*).

Sit in a meditation posture and fix the eyes on one point without blinking. At first the eyes may water or dry out, but with practice they become accustomed to the steady gaze. Begin by gazing for only three to five minutes and gradually increase the duration.

Nauli (*Intestinal Wash*)

Nauli means "pipe", referring to the pipelike appearance of the abdominal recti as they are contracted. In this technique the abdominal muscles are isolated (by contraction) and rotated.

Stand with feet apart and knees slightly bent. Place hands on thighs just above the knees, fingers pointing toward each other. Exhale all air. Without inhaling, pull the stomach up and back and try to push just the abdominal recti forward. Still not breathing, rotate these muscles from left to right, then right to left several times.

Nauli should be practiced early in the morning; it increases heat in the navel area, which aids digestion and elimination. People with ulcers should not practice *nauli*.

Kapala Bhati (*Skull Shining*)

See *Four Purifications* on page 20.

FOUR PURIFICATIONS

In ancient times yogis used the *shat karma* for purifying the nerve channels (*nadis*). Since the *shat karma* are quite strenuous, and some of them can be dangerous, teachers of Yoga devised a simpler method of purification, which consists of four different techniques put together. Hence the practice is named *Four Purifications.*

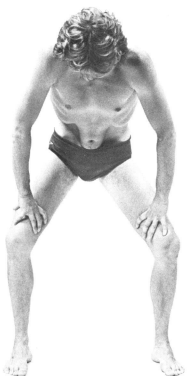

Nauli

These four techniques must be practiced for two to three months before beginning regular *pranayama*. Do them in the order given. Sit in a meditation posture with eyes closed, concentrating on *ajna chakra*.

Nadishodhana
(Alternate Nostril Breathing)

Gently exhale all air. Close the right nostril with the thumb of the right hand, and inhale slowly and deeply through the left nostril. Close the left nostril with the ring finger, releasing the thumb, and exhale through the right. Inhale through the right, then close it with the thumb and exhale through the left. This makes one round. Begin with ten rounds and gradually increase to forty.

Kapala Bhati
(Skull Shining) (arms straight)

Kapala bhati is a series of forced exhalations: exhale and inhale quickly and lightly through both nostrils, feeling energy striking the point behind the eyebrow center. Emphasize the exhale, letting the inhalation come as a natural reflex. After one series of exhalations, which sould last no longer than one minute, rest and breathe naturally. Then repeat. Begin with three rounds of thirty exhalations each and increase gradually to ten rounds of sixty each.

This method purifies the head area which calms the thoughts. In this way the rapid breathing of *kapala bhati* induces a calm mind and calm breath. Persons with high blood pressure or lung disease should not practice *kapala bhati*. *Kapala bhati* is also one of the *Shat Karma*. (See page 19.)

Agnisara Dhauti
(Fire Wash) (come fwd on hand)

Inhale, then exhale all air. While holding the breath out, pull the abdomen up and toward the backbone; release it suddenly. Repeat this in-and-out movement rapidly as long as the breath can be held out without strain. Then inhale gently. Start with three rounds and increase gradually to ten, beginning with thirty pulls and increasing to sixty in each breath.

This method strengthens *uddiyana bandha* and creates heat at the navel center *(manipura chakra)*, which purifies the *nadis* and stimulates the digestive system.

Ashvini Mudra (arms bent)
(Horse Mudra)

Inhale completely and hold the breath. Contract and release the anal sphincter rapidly and repeatedly. Hold the breath only so long as the following exhalation can be slow and controlled. Begin with three rounds of thirty pulls each, and increase gradually to ten rounds of sixty each.

Ashvini mudra strengthens *mula bandha* and pushes *prana* upward.

"The world is an abstract art. We see it as we want to see it. It is a garden of roses and it is also a forest of thorny bushes and poison oak."

20

Four Purifications
(Intermediate Method)

In this method, the *Four Purifications* are done in such a way that there are no 'rest breaths' in between. (Note: This method may be added after practicing the *Four Purifications* separately every day for three to six months.

Do ten rounds of *nadishodhana*. After the last exhalation out the left nostril, inhale partially through both nostrils and immediately begin *kapala bhati*. At the end of one series of *kapala bhati* exhalations, inhale slowly and completely, then exhale all air, hold the breath out, and do *agnisara dhauti*. After a round of *agnisara dhauti*, inhale completely, hold the breath, and do *ashvini mudra*. Exhale completely out the nostrils and begin again with *nadishodhana*. Do five rounds, gradually increasing the numbers and retentions.

TRI BANDHA
(Three Locks)

Three *bandhas* (body locks) are used in the practice of *pranayama*, which help to control the flow of *prana*. Mastery of the *bandhas* insures correct *prana-yama*, so these three methods should be practiced carefully for three months before beginning *pranayama*.

Mula Bandha
(Anal Lock)

Sit in any meditation posture. (*Siddhasana* is best for this method.) Inhale slowly and completely, contracting and lifting the anal sphincter muscle. Exhale slowly and release. Start with ten rounds, gradually increasing to twenty.

When the technique is perfected and used with *pranayama*, contract slowly with inhalation, hold the contraction during retention, and release slowly with exhalation. *Mula bandha* causes *apana vayu*, which normally flows downward, to rise and unite with *prana vayu* at the navel center, which then awakens *kundalini*. *Mula bandha* increases concentration, strengthens the reproductive glands, and stimulates the gastric fire.

Jalandhara Bandha
(Throat Lock)

Sit in a meditation posture. Inhale slowly; then bend the head forward and press the chin tightly into the hollow of the neck, keeping the spine straight. This stops the

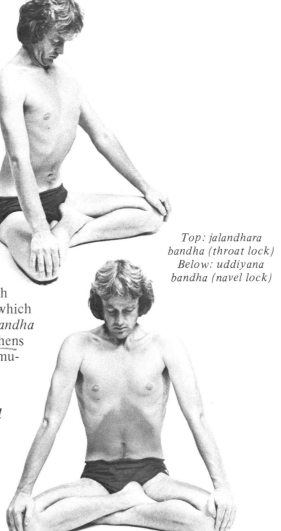

Top: jalandhara bandha (throat lock) Below: uddiyana bandha (navel lock)

breath. Hold as long as possible without strain. Raise the chin; then exhale slowly. Begin with ten rounds and increase gradually to twenty rounds.

According to Yoga physiology a subtle nectar flows from *sahasrara chakra*, falls to *manipura chakra*, and is consumed by the gastric fire. *Jalandhara bandha* prevents the nectar from falling, which brings calmness, long life, and good health. Thus the name *jalandhara*, which means "cloud-holding, receptacle of vital fluid".

Jalandhara bandha presses on *vishuddha chakra* where there is a network of subtle nerves. By pressing the chin tightly against this center, the movement of energy in sixteen centers is stopped, which brings infinite peace.

Uddiyana Bandha
(Navel Lock)

Place hands, fingers pointing inward, on thighs just above the knees. Exhale slowly and completely. With breath held out, pull the abdomen up and in as far as possible toward the spine. Hold as long as comfortable. Relax and inhale slowly. Exhale and do another round. Start with ten rounds, gradually increasing to twenty rounds.

Uddiyana bandha pushes *prana* into *sushumna*, forcing *kundalini* upward. Thus the name *uddiyana*, which means "flying up". *Uddiyana bandha* increases gastric fire; strengthens the lungs; and alleviates indigestion, abdominal diseases, and menstrual disorders.

"When the mind is purified by sadhana, *its first symptom is dispassion. And then knowledge dawns in the mind."*

22

PRANAYAMA
(Breath Control)
— control of lifeforce

Pranayama is best learned from an experienced teacher. Practice regularly with a positive attitude; a lot of *pranayama* one day and little or nothing the next day is improper practice. *Pranayama* must not be forced; if it is, one can damage the brain, heart, or lungs. If any adverse physical symptom appears due to wrong *pranayama*, stop immediately and do *viparita karani mudra* (see page 39). If symptoms continue, stop all *pranayama* and do only the *Four Purifications & Eight Kriyas*. Consult a teacher. People with ulcers, heart or lung disease should not do *pranayama;* they can do the *Eight Kriyas*.

Perspiration generated by *pranayama* should be rubbed back into the body, as it is charged with electrical energy *(ojas)* and makes the body strong.

Pranayama is practiced on an empty stomach; wait at least two hours after eating. Wear loose clothing and sit on a thick mat or blanket in a meditation pose (see page 46), with the back, neck, and head in a straight line. Concentration is on *ajna chakra.* (3rd eye)

Tribandha Pranayama
(Three Locks Breath)

Inhale slowly through both nostrils and apply *mula bandha.* Then hold the breath and apply *jalandhara bandha.* Lift head, exhale slowly and smoothly and simultaneously squeeze the stomach in with *uddiyana bandha.* Begin with ten rounds and gradually increase to twenty.

Tribandha pranayama purifies the *nadis* and awakens *kundalini.*

Dirgha Rechak
(Long Exhale Breath)

Inhale normally; then exhale as slowly and smoothly as possible. Concentrate on the exhalation, making it long, smooth, and subtle. Inhale again normally, and start another round. Begin with ten rounds and gradually increase to twenty.

Dirgha rechak makes the exhalation long and subtle. It strengthens *prana,* digestion, the lungs, and sharpens the mind and memory.

Dirgha Purak
(Long Inhale Breath)

Exhale normally; then inhale as slowly and smoothly as possible. Concentrate on the inhalation, making it long, smooth, and subtle. Exhale normally and start another round. Begin with ten rounds, gradually increasing to twenty.

Dirgha purak makes the inhalation long and subtle. It strengthens *prana,* digestion, the lungs, and sharpens the mind and memory.

Ujjayi *(Victorious Breath)*

Ujjayi means "victorious." By this *pranayama* one gains control over *prana. Ujjayi* has a heating effect. Before practicing, wash the tongue and rinse the throat to loosen phlegm.

Ujjayi can be done sitting, standing, or even walking. Close the mouth and bend the head slightly forward, pulling the chin back a little. Inhale through both nostrils, drawing the air across the throat by slightly closing the glottis. As the air passes through the flattened glottis, a soft breathing or rubbing sound is made in the throat. Hold the breath for four to five seconds; then raise the chin, close the right nostril, and exhale through the left. The exhalation should be twice the length of the inhalation. Begin with ten rounds and increase to forty over a period of three months. **Note**: *In* Ujjayi *one may also exhale through both nostrils.*

Ujjayi removes phlegm in the throat, increases appetite, and is helpful for cough and fever.

Shitali *(Cooling Breath)*

Fold the tongue with the sides upward so it is like a tube, and extend it beyond the lips. Inhale slowly through this tube with a hissing sound; then swallow the air into the stomach and hold the breath for four or five seconds without the *bandhas.* Exhale slowly

"The world is not a burden; we make it a burden by our desires. When the desires are removed, the world is as light as a feather on an elephant's back."

23

through both nostrils. Begin with ten rounds and gradually increase to forty.

Shitali has a cooling effect, so it should not be done in cold weather. It is helpful in cases of indigestion, bilious disorders, and colic.

Sitkari *(Hissing Breath)*

Sitkari is a variation of *shitali* for those who cannot curl the tongue. Flatten the tongue and press it on the back of the teeth, or place the tongue between the teeth. Part the lips slightly so that air slips by the sides of the tongue while inhaling with a hissing sound. Continue as in *shitali*.

Bhramari
(Bee Humming)

Tilt the head forward, constrict the throat muscles, and make as high-pitched a sound as possible while inhaling through the nostrils. The sound is not from the vocal cords but from air passing through the constricted throat. After inhaling, hold the breath for three seconds; then exhale making the same sound. The exhalation should be slower than the inhalation and with a higher-pitched tone. Begin with five rounds and gradually increase to forty. *Bhramari* awakens the inner sound *(nada)* which dissolves the mind and brings *samadhi*. Typical sounds that appear are: crickets, bee, conch, birds, flute, bell, cymbals, trumpet, kettle-drum, thunder, and finally the pure sound of *anahata nada* (Om) arises from the heart. *Bhramari* is recommended for vocal musicians.

Bhastrika *(Bellows Breath)*

Bhastrika is an intermediate *pranayama,* which may be added to one's *sadhana* after practicing beginning *pranayama* daily for three to six months.

Sit in a meditation pose. Inhale fully and expand the abdomen; then exhale completely with a little force, contracting the diaphragm. Emphasis is on the exhalation. Inhale again and repeat. After twenty exhalations, inhale slowly with *mula bandha,* apply *jalandhara bandha,* and hold the breath as long as possible without strain. Then exhale slowly, applying *uddiyana bandha.* This makes one round. Do three rounds.

Bhastrika is a moderate *pranayama;* it lengthens breath retention, awakens *kundalini,* and purifies the *nadis.*

Sahita Kumbhaka
(Breath With Retention)

Sahita kumbhaka means "together with breath retention." It is an intermediate *pranayama,* and may be added after practicing beginning *pranayama* daily for three to six months.

This *pranayama* is done with a ratio

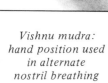

Vishnu mudra:
hand position used
in alternate
nostril breathing

of 1:4:2 for inhalation, retention, and exhalation respectively. Begin by using four seconds to inhale, sixteen to retain the breath, and eight to exhale, with just a one second hold after exhalation.

Sit in a meditation posture. Exhale completely. Close the right nostril with *vishnu mudra* (page 24) and inhale in four seconds through the left nostril, applying *mula bandha*. Hold the breath for sixteen seconds while applying *jalandhara bandha*. Then lift head and exhale through the right nostril for eight seconds, using *uddiyana bandha*. Hold the breath out for one second without *bandhas*. Repeat this sequence on the opposite side. This constitutes one round. Begin with five rounds, gradually increasing to forty rounds. (**Note:** Increase the duration of inhalation, retention, and exhalation gradually, i.e. 5:20:10, 6:24:12, 8:32:16.)

Sahita kumbhaka is a moderate *pranayama*. It purifies the body and awakens *kundalini*.

Eight Kriyas (Swasa Yam)

This is a series of simple breathing exercises that are safe for anyone. They are a preparation for *pranayama*, and are also used before meditation as a practice of *pratyahara*. The word *kriya* means "method" or "action." Here it means a method for calming the mind.

Sit with head, neck, and spine in a straight line. The breath should be slow, deep, and gentle—do not force or strain. These exercises involve two types of breath: a chest breath, used when inhaling through the nostrils, and a stomach breath, used when inhaling through the mouth. In the first, the chest expands fully and the abdomen presses in slightly; in the second, the chest does not fully expand and the abdomen pushes out. **Note:** Do the *Eight Kriyas* after *pranayama* or right before methods of concentration and meditation.

Kriya 1: Inhale into the chest slowly, gently, and deeply through both nostrils, pulling the abdomen in slightly. Exhale slowly and gently, also through both nostrils. Do this five times.

Kriya 2: Inhale into the chest slowly, gently, and deeply through both nostrils, pulling the abdomen in slightly. Exhale slowly and gently through a partially-open mouth. Do this five times.

Kriya 3: Inhale into the stomach slowly, gently, and deeply through the mouth with slightly extended lips, letting the abdomen push out. Exhale slowly and gently through both nostrils, pulling the abdomen in slightly. Do this five times.

Kriya 4: Closing the right nostril with right thumb, inhale into the chest through the left nostril, pulling the abdomen in slightly. Lift the thumb, close the left nostril with ring finger, and exhale slowly and gently through the right nostril. Do this five times.

Kriya 5: Closing the left nostril with right ring finger, inhale into the chest through the right nostril, pulling the ab-

"There is always fear in everything. But we have to face the fear, fight with the fear, and finish it forever."

25

domen in slightly. Close right nostril with thumb, exhale slowly and gently through the left. Do this five times.

Kriya 6: Exhale slowly and gently through both nostrils, completely emptying the lungs. The abdomen sucks in. Let the following breath through the nostrils come in as a natural reflex (a normal, not a deep breath), as the abdomen is released. Do this five times.

Kriya 7: Inhale into the stomach slowly and deeply through the mouth with slightly extended lips, letting the abdomen push out. Exhale slowly and gently through the mouth, pulling the abdomen in slightly. Do this five times.

Kriya 8: Inhale deeply into the chest through both nostrils in five slow sips, pulling the abdomen in slightly. Exhale slowly and gently through the mouth. Do this five times.

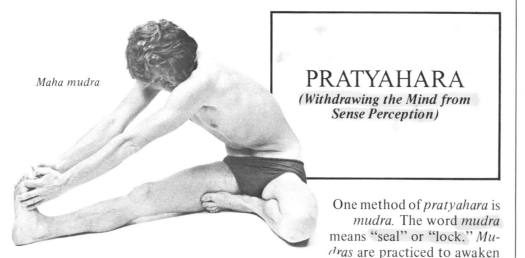

Maha mudra

PRATYAHARA
(Withdrawing the Mind from Sense Perception)

One method of *pratyahara* is *mudra.* The word *mudra* means "seal" or "lock." *Mudras* are practiced to awaken and direct the flow of *kundalini,* to induce stillness and strength, and to "lock in" the benefits from the other practices. The "Hand Mudras" (see page 60) can be safely practiced from the beginning. The following *mudras* are intermediate methods, to be added to one's *sadhana* after doing beginning methods every day for three to six months.

Maha Mudra *(Great Seal)*

This is the most important *mudra* for pushing *prana* upward and awakening *kundalini.*

Sit with both legs stretched forward; fold the left leg and press the perineum with the heel of the left foot. Without bending the right leg, grab the big toe of the right foot with both hands. Inhale slowly and completely through the nostrils, applying *mula bandha.* When the lungs are full, apply all three *bandhas* and hold the breath as long as possible, concentrating on *ajna chakra.* Raise the head, then exhale slowly and gently through the nostrils. Reverse legs and repeat. Start with two *mudras* on each side and gradually increase to ten.

Note: Beginners can practice this *mudra* after perfecting the three *bandhas.*

Maha Bandha Mudra
(Great Lock)

Sit with left heel pressing the perineum, and place the right foot over the left thigh. Inhale slowly through the nostrils, applying *mula bandha.* When the lungs are full, apply *jalandhara bandha* and hold the breath as long as possible without strain. Concentrate on *ajna chakra.* Exhale slowly while raising the head and gradually applying *uddiyana bandha.* Switch legs and repeat. Begin with two on each side and gradually increase to ten.

Note: A variation is to slowly release and contract *mula bandha* three times while holding the breath.

Maha Vedha Mudra
(Great Piercing Mudra)

Sit in *Siddhasana* (page 46) or *Padmasana* (page 46) with palms resting flat on the floor beside buttocks. Inhale slowly with *mula bandha,* hold breath with *jalandhara bandha,* and concentrate on *ajna chakra.* Lift the body up and balance on the hands; then drop to the floor suddenly, landing on the buttocks. Release *bandhas* and exhale slowly. Begin with two and gradually increase to ten.

Shaktichalana Mudra
(Energy-Moving Mudra)

Sit in *Padmasana* or *Siddhasana* with palms flat on the floor beside buttocks. Lift the body and strike the buttocks gently on the floor twenty to twenty-five times. Then inhale through the nostrils, applying *mula bandha.* Hold breath with *jalandhara bandha* and unite *prana vayu* with *apana vayu.*

While holding the breath, do *ashvini mudra.* Then exhale slowly through the nostrils. Begin by doing three times and gradually increase to ten. After finishing *shaktichalana mudra* sit with a calm mind and meditate. This *mudra* helps in awakening *kundalini.* **Note:** A variation is to inhale through the left nostril, do the *mudra,* and exhale through the right nostril.

Maha vedha mudra

DHYANA
(Meditation)

In meditation the breath is relaxed and natural, as in sleep: on the inhalation the abdomen extends slightly forward, and on the exhalation it draws in slightly.

To withdraw the mind from external objects *(pratyahara)* and prepare the mind for meditation, do *japa* (mental repetition) of *OM* or any name of

"Faith and devotion are the foundation on which meditation is built."

27

"There is no peace in the world. If there is any peace, it is only in meditation. At first everyone does false meditation. But this false meditation turns into true meditation by regular practice."

God, then the twenty-four hand *mudras* (page 61), prayers, and the *Eight Kriyas*. Then practice a meditation of your choice. Right after meditation do the eight hand *mudras* (page 65).

MEDITATION ON THE BREATH

Sit in a meditation posture with eyes closed. Fix the mind on the process of breathing. During inhalation the breath flows down from the nostrils to the abdomen, and the abdomen pushes out slightly. During exhalation the breath flows up from the abdomen to the nostrils, and the abdomen pulls in slightly. Concentrate on this movement. The breath should be very relaxed. As the breath becomes calm, the mind becomes calm and one-pointed.

AJAPA MANTRA MEDITATION

Sit in a comfortable meditation posture with eyes closed. Concentrate on the breath rising and falling. Hear the sound *HAM** with inhalation and the sound *SAH* with exhalation. Meditate on this sound of the breath.

SUSHUMNA

Inhale consciously and visualize the breath going down from the nostrils to the navel *chakra*. Exhale and watch the breath rise from the navel *chakra* and

**M̊* indicates a nasal sound, somewhat like "ng" in English.

28

go out through the nostrils. Do this eleven times.

Inhale consciously and visualize the breath going from the nostrils down to the navel *chakra*. The breath is spreading a vital energy throughout the body. Your head, your chest, your abdomen, arms, and legs—all are filled with this *prana*. As you exhale imagine all impurities—anger, hate, jealousy, ego, lust, attachment—are departing from every pore of your body. Do this eleven times.

Now as the breath goes down to the navel *chakra* a feeling of bliss spreads all over your body. In your head, in your heart, in your abdomen, in your limbs—all is bliss. As you exhale feel the bliss spreading all around you. Do this eleven times.

Visualize a line of light running from *muladhara chakra* to *ajna chakra*. It is the thickness of a hair and very bright. Gradually it grows in diameter.

Now it is as thick as your little finger and growing more luminous.

Now it is as thick as your middle finger, and still more luminous.

Now it is as thick as your thumb, still growing more luminous.

Now a column of light is standing inside of you, from *muladhara* to *ajna*. It is spreading all around you.

Now you are in the middle of a light shaped like an egg. Concentrate on the egg-shaped light surrounding you for fifteen minutes.

Now the egg shape is changing into a column of light.

Now the light is as thin as your

thumb.

Now the light is as thin as your middle finger.

Now the light is as thin as your little finger.

Now the line of light is like a hair connecting *muladhara* to *ajna*.

Now chant *Om*.

SPACE

Sit in a meditation posture with eyes closed or fixed on the tip of your nose. Visualize the space within each cell of your body. Imagine the cell walls dissolving and feel your body filled with space like the sky. Imagine the space of your body merging with the space of the room where you are sitting. The space in the room merges with infinite space. Now all barriers are dissolved. Fix the mind in infinite space.

FULL MOON

Sit in a meditation posture with eyes closed and visualize the full moon shining inside your head. The moonlight is spreading out, filling the space inside of you and all around you. Nothing stops the light, as it spreads to infinity. Dissolve the mind in that light.

SURRENDER

Sit in a meditation posture. Any thought that comes to the mind should be diverted toward the infinite God. Realize that everything is created by God so any thought that comes should go back to its source. Surrender all thoughts and merge the mind into God.

ASANA
(Posture, Seat)

Asana conditions the body so that one can 'sit' easily; in this sense it is a preparation for *pranayama* and meditation. In one's daily routine, however, it is preferable to practice *pranayama* and meditation before *asana*, as doing *asanas* stimulates the mind, which is a hindrance in meditation.

Sunrise and sunset are the best times to practice *asanas*. Choose a quiet, well-ventilated place away from people. Put a thick blanket or a pad on the floor to protect the body from cold and bruising. Wear comfortable, loose clothing.

A bath before *asanas* helps loosen tight muscles, but after *asanas* one should wait twenty minutes before bathing.

Asanas should not be practiced when there is food in the stomach—wait for three hours after a meal. After finishing *asanas* wait twenty minutes before eating.

In the case of serious illness *asanas* should not be practiced without consulting an experienced teacher. Do

"The body is a boat which carries the soul in the ocean of the world. If it is not strong, or it has a hole, then it can't cross the ocean. So the first duty is to fix the boat."

*"It's hard
to be responsible
for our own progress.
We always seek for
someone to carry us and
put us on some
higher level.
We have to understand
that our progress
is based on our
own efforts."*

not do *asanas* if there is fever. Women should avoid inverted poses during the first three days of menses.

Generally, *asanas* are practiced slowly; but to gain flexibility in the beginning, one may move quickly through various *asanas*. Do not overexert or force the body into any posture—do *asanas* according to your strength and flexibility, adding new poses and increasing the duration slowly. Awareness, concentration, and effort are more important than the ability to physically accomplish a difficult pose.

Beginners should do *asanas* without breath retention for three months. Later, when retaining the breath, hold only as long as it is comfortable—do not strain. One may prefer to hold some poses for several minutes, in which case one should inhale or exhale as indicated; then breathe naturally while holding the pose.

Always inhale and exhale through the nostrils unless specified differently. The breath should be smooth, slow, and deep. Likewise the body movement should be slow and thoughtful, in harmony with the breath. Complete synthesis of mind (concentration), body (movement), and breath is perfection in the practice of *asanas*.

After each series, or after several strenuous *asanas,* do the *Relaxation Pose* (page 55) for fifteen or twenty seconds. Upon finishing *asanas* it is important to do the *Relaxation Pose* for five to ten minutes. Then sit in a quiet place with a peaceful mind.

All balancing poses are good for the mind. They improve circulation and memory, and they alleviate nervous disorders.

All *asanas* in which the body is lifted up and rests on the hands are good for the reproductive glands.

All *asanas* in which the head is lower than the body are good for the pineal, pituitary, and thyroid glands, as well as the lungs.

All *asanas* in which the body bends toward the feet are good for the adrenal glands and also push *prana* upward.

Warm-Ups

It is important to always do some warm-up exercises before *asanas*. The following routine, or any exercises that increase circulation throughout the body, may be done:

Stand and rub the palms together briskly; then massage face and entire body. Run in place, or hop on both feet. Vigorously shake the whole body—be loose. Let the head fall forward, backward, and from side to side. With arms outstretched to either side, do some arm-circling—forward and backward. Reach straight up and stretch as high as possible; then, keeping legs straight, bend forward letting the head and arms fall toward the floor.

Sit on the floor with legs crossed, hold the feet with the hands, and roll gently backward and forward on the spine. Stretch both legs straight out in front; then grab one foot with both

30

hands and pull it up to the right ear and then to the left ear. Now take it around in large circles, first away from the body and then toward the body, letting the knee fall to the side as the leg bends. Repeat with opposite leg. Place soles of feet together, clasp hands around feet, and pull them as close to the body as possible. Then press the knees down toward the floor. Place hands on knees and push down gently—do not strain. Stretch legs straight forward again, and "shake them out", by alternately slapping the backs of legs on the floor.

Salutation to the Sun
(Surya Namaskara)

This exercise is a good way to begin the practice of *asana*. It is actually a *mudra* composed of a group of *asanas*, put together so as to form a rhythmical movement and a complete exercise for the whole body.

Surya Namaskara was originally designed by ancient yogis according to the phases of the sun. Each of the twelve postures corresponds to one of the sun's twelve phases.

The sun descends for six months and then ascends for six months. In the same way *Surya Namaskara* has six descending postures and six ascending postures. This sequence of twelve postures constitutes one round of *Surya Namaskara,* and six to twelve rounds are done as part of one's daily routine.

Mantras can also be combined with *Surya Namaskara,* augmenting its physical and spiritual benefits. There are twelve *mantras,* and each is a salutation to one of the life-giving qualities of the sun. Thus, when using the *mantras* it is necessary to do twelve rounds of *Surya Namaskara.*

Stand with arms at sides, take a deep inhalation and chant the *mantra* as loudly as possible; this exercises the chest, lungs, and vocal cords. Then do one round of postures, chant the second *mantra,* do another round, etc.

1. *Om Hrām Mitrāya Namah*—I salute the sun energy of friendship.
2. *Om Hrīm Ravaye Namah*—I salute the sun, who is the Divider.
3. *Om Hrūm Suryāya Namah*—I salute the sun, who is luminous.
4. *Om Hraim Bhānave Namah*—I salute the sun, who is shining.
5. *Om Hraum Khagāya Namah*—I salute the sun, wanderer of space.
6. *Om Hrah Pushneya Namah*—I salute the sun, who is the nourisher.
7. *Om Hrām Hiranyagarbhāya Namah*—I salute the sun, the golden embryo.
8. *Om Hrīm Marīchaye Namah*—I salute the sun who is light.
9. *Om Hrūm Ādityāya Namah*—I salute the sun, the source of the world.
10. *Om Hraim Savītre Namah*—I salute the sun, the procreator.
11. *Om Hraum Arkāya Namah*—I salute the radiant sun.
12. *Om Hrah Bhāskarāya Namah*—I salute the sun, maker of light.

"A path alone can't bring salvation. One who walks on that path with steady feet attains salvation. It doesn't matter what path you choose it will take you to the same God."

31

SALUTATION TO THE SUN
(Surya Namaskara)

1. Upward Salutation Pose *(Urdhva Namaskarasana):* Inhale slowly and bend backward, raising and stretching the arms above the head.

2. Hands to Feet Pose *(Hastapadasana):* Exhale slowly and bend forward, keeping the knees straight. Place palms of hands on the floor beside the feet, touch forehead to knees, and press chin toward chest.

3. One Foot Extended Pose *(Eka Pada Prasaranasana):* Inhale slowly and raise the chin; stretch the left leg straight back while bending right knee in front of chest. Keeping palms flat on the floor, stretch the head and shoulders back and upward.

4. Mountain Pose *(Bhudrasana):* Exhale slowly and raise the buttocks, keeping arms and legs straight. The head should be between the arms, chin pressed into chest, heels on the floor.

5. Snake Pose *(Sarpasana):* Inhale slowly and, keeping arms and legs straight, lower pelvis to the floor. Push up and back into the Snake Pose, keeping shoulders raised and tilting head back.

6. Eight Parts Bowing Pose *(Ashtanga Paranipatasana):* Exhale slowly and lower the body, touching the forehead, chest, knees, and toes to the floor. The hips should be slightly lifted. Counting the hands, eight parts of the body touch the floor.

7. Snake Pose *(Sarpasana):* Inhale slowly, raising the head and chest by straightening the arms. Push up and back into the Snake Pose, keeping shoulders raised and tilting the head back.

8. Mountain Pose *(Bhudrasana):* Exhale slowly and raise the buttocks, keeping arms and legs straight. The head should be between the arms, chin pressed into chest, heels on the floor.

9. One Foot Extended Pose *(Eka Pada Prasaranasana):* Inhale slowly and bring the left foot forward, bending the knee up to chest. The right leg remains stretched backward. With both palms flat on the floor, stretch the head and shoulders up and back.

10. Hands to Feet Pose *(Hasta Padasana):* Exhale slowly and bring the right foot up beside the left, straightening the knees. Both palms remain flat on the floor beside the feet. Press chin toward chest and bring forehead to knees.

11. Upward Salutation Pose *(Urdhva Namaskarasana):* Inhale slowly and raise the body, keeping arms stretched above the head. Arch the back and bend backward as in posture one.

12. Salutation Pose *(Namaskarasana):* Exhale slowly and bring arms down; join palms in front of chest, fingers pointing upward.

Benefits: Fortifies the whole body, stimulating circulation and giving strength and flexibility to the spine; energizes the nerve channels, heart, lungs, and digestive organs.

33

PALM TREE
(Tadasana)

Stand with feet together. Inhale slowly, swing arms up over head, and raise up on tiptoe. Hold the breath* in pose; then exhale slowly, lowering arms and heels. *Note:* This pose can also be done by raising one arm at a time. **Benefits:** Develops concentration and steadiness of mind.

EAGLE POSE *(Garudasana)*

Wrap left foot around right leg, crossing over the front and hooking left foot behind right calf. Cross arms (left over right) at elbows and wrap lower arms around each other. Place palms together, fingers pointing upward. Inhale and bend the knees, keeping the back vertical. Hold breath in pose; then exhale while coming up. Reverse arms and legs and repeat. **Benefits:** Develops balance, concentration, and memory; strengthens ankles, legs, spine, and reproductive glands.

TREE POSE
(Vrikshasana)

Stand with feet together. Raise left foot and rest it either on top of the right thigh or with the sole pressing the inside of the right thigh. Place arms either in front of chest or above head, with palms together and fingers pointing upward. Fix the gaze on any object at eye level to maintain balance. Hold pose for five to fifteen minutes, breathing normally. **Benefits:** Develops balance and memory; calms the mind.

ANGULAR POSE I *(Konasana)*

Stand with feet apart, arms outstretched to either side. Exhale and slowly twist torso. Touch right hand to left foot, extending left arm straight up. Turn head to look up at left hand. Hold breath out in pose; then inhale slowly and come up. Repeat on other side. **Benefits**: Improves balance, concentration, flexibility, and circulation; strengthens the spine, abdomen, chest, and lungs.

ANGULAR POSE II *(Konasana)*

Stand with feet apart, arms outstretched to sides. Exhale slowly and bend sideways, raising left arm straight up and trying to touch right arm to right foot. Hold breath out in pose; then inhale coming back up. Repeat on other side. **Benefits**: Same as for Angular Pose I.

*Note: Whenever breath retention is indicated, hold for five to twenty seconds, or as long as comfortable.

35

ANGULAR POSE III *(Konasana)*

Stand with feet wide apart, arms outstretched to either side.
Exhale and slowly bend right knee, lunging sideways until
right hand touches floor on outside of right foot.
Stretch left arm over the head, parallel to the floor.
Hold breath out in pose; then inhale
and come up. Repeat on other side.
Benefits: Same as for Angular Pose 1.

ANGULAR POSE IV
(Konasana)

Do Angular Pose 3. Bring lower arm in
front of bent knee and under thigh, then
bend upper arm and clasp hands behind
back. Look up. Hold breath out during
pose; then inhale and come up.
Repeat on other side. **Benefits:**
Same as for Angular Pose 1.

36

STANDING HEAD-KNEE TOUCH
(Utthita Janusparshasana)

Stand with feet apart, hands on hips. Exhale slowly and bend forehead down toward left knee, placing hands on either side of left foot (or grabbing left ankle). Hold breath out in pose; then inhale and come up. Repeat on other side. **Benefits**: Same as for Angular Pose 1.

HEAD TO TOE TOUCH
(Viryastambhanasana)

Stand with feet wide apart. Clasp hands behind the back. Exhale, bend right knee, and lunge slowly to the right, touching forehead to the right foot. Hold breath in pose; then inhale slowly and come up. Repeat on other side. **Benefits**: Strengthens the legs, reproductive glands, and nervous system; improves circulation, and tones abdominal organs.

SHOULDERSTAND
(Sarvangasana)

Lie flat on the back, arms parallel to body. Inhale slowly and raise legs until they make a right angle with the body. Then, with arms flat on floor, raise body straight up on shoulders so it makes a right angle with the head. Balance on the shoulders, breathing naturally, for five to ten minutes. *Note:* This pose can also be done with hands supporting back. **Benefits:** Strengthens the entire body; regulates the thyroid and para-thyroid glands, which control metabolism; promotes healthy functioning of the circulatory, respiratory, alimentary, genito-urinary, and nervous systems; keeps the spine elastic; reduces fat; and prolongs youth.

PLOW POSE *(Halasana)*

From the Shoulderstand exhale slowly and lower legs down over head. Keeping knees and arms straight, touch the floor with toes. Hold breath out in pose; then inhale slowly and return to Shoulderstand, or inhale slowly, then exhale into the Ear-Knee Pose. *Note:* The Plow Pose is complementary to the Bow Pose. **Benefits:** Same as for Shoulderstand. In addition it tones spinal nerves, muscles of the back, and the sympathetic nervous system. Makes the spine flexible, prevents laziness, and relieves constipation.

EAR-KNEE POSE
(Karna Pidasana)

From the Plow Pose exhale slowly and bend legs, bringing knees forward to cover ears. Hold breath out in pose; then inhale slowly and return to Plow Pose. **Benefits:** In addition to the benefits of Shoulderstand and Plow Pose, the Ear-Knee Pose helps in hearing inner sound, *nada.*

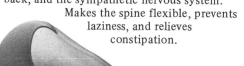

ON-THE-BACK SERIES 38

REVERSE POSTURE MUDRA
(Viparita Karani Mudra)

Lie on the back, arms at sides. Inhale slowly and raise legs until they make a right angle with the body. Keeping elbows on floor, raise torso and support hips with hands. Legs should be vertical. Hold breath in pose; then exhale while lowering legs to floor. *Note:* If one is doing this *mudra* to correct adverse effects of improper *pranayama* practice, the pose should be held as long as possible, breathing normally. **Benefits:** Preserves the subtle nectar that flows from *sahasrara chakra*, promoting strength and energy.

BRIDGE POSE
(Setuasana)

Do the Shoulderstand (or Viparita Karani Mudra). Supporting back or buttocks with hands, exhale and slowly lower legs until feet touch floor. In the beginning knees are bent; when perfected the legs are straight, with toes touching floor. Hold breath out in pose; then inhale and return to Shoulderstand. **Benefits:** Expands the chest, tones the kidneys, makes the spine flexible, and cures backache.

39

FISH POSE
(Matsyasana)

Lie on the back with arms at sides. By pushing on floor with elbows, inhale slowly and arch back so the top of head rests on floor. Raise chest as high as possible. Place hands on chest, palms together, with fingers pointing toward chin. Hold breath in pose; then exhale slowly and return to starting position. *Note:* The Fish is a counterpose for the Shoulderstand, and is complementary to the Rabbit Pose. **Benefits:** Expands the chest, strengthens the lungs, and brings fresh blood to the thyroid and parathyroid glands. Helpful for asthma and bronchitis.

WHEEL POSE
(Chakrasana)

Lie on back. Put hands beside ears, palms down and fingers pointing toward feet. Bend knees and pull feet close to buttocks. Inhale slowly and raise body up, balancing on hands and feet. Hold breath in pose; then exhale while lowering body back to floor. **Benefits:** Tones the whole body, especially the spine; strengthens the arms; and gives vitality, energy, and a feeling of lightness.

40

LEG-HAND LIFTING POSE
(Uttana Hasta Padasana)

Lie on the back. Inhale and slowly lift legs and torso, holding arms straight out in front, and balance on the hips. Hold breath in pose; then exhale lowering body to floor. *Note:* This pose is complementary to the Full Alligator Pose. **Benefits:** Strengthens the heart, lungs, chest, and abdomen; increases gastric fire; prevents hernia; and can relieve headache.

LEG LIFTING POSE
(Uttana Padasana)

Lie on back. Inhale and raise legs slowly until they are at a 45° angle to the floor, keeping lower back pressed to floor. Hold breath in pose; then exhale lowering feet to floor. *Notes:* A variation is to circle legs several times clockwise, next counterclockwise, then in opposite directions inward and outward. The Leg Lifting Pose is complementary to the Half Locust Pose. **Benefits:** Strengthens the abdomen, legs, reproductive glands, and the lumbar region of the back; tones the abdominal organs; and relieves gastric troubles.

WIND-RELEASING POSE
(Pavana Muktasana)

Lie on back. Inhale and fold left knee up to chest, pulling it tight by clasping hands around it. Try to touch head to knee, keeping right leg straight. Hold breath in pose; then exhale while lowering leg and head. Repeat with right leg; then with both legs together. **Benefits:** Releases trapped gas in the stomach, cures constipation and indigestion, and reduces abdominal fat.

HEAD TO KNEE POSE
(Janushirshasana)

Sit with legs straight out in front. Fold left leg in so
that the heel presses the groin and the knee
remains out at the side. Inhale slowly and grab
the right big toe with both hands. Exhale and
pull the body forward, touching forehead
to right knee. Hold the breath out in pose;
then inhale slowly, returning to sitting
position. Switch legs and repeat. **Benefits**:
Increases gastric fire, tones the kidneys, and strengthens the spine.

Sit on floor, stretching legs straight forward. Inhale slowly and grab big toes with
hands. Exhale and bend forward, touching forehead to knees. (If possible
clasp hands around the feet or lay hands beside feet.) Hold breath out in pose;
then inhale slowly and return to sitting position. *Note:* The Back Stretching
Pose is complementary to the Cobra Pose. **Benefits**: Increases gastric fire and
intestinal peristalsis, thus alleviating digestive disorders; massages the spinal
column; strengthens the nervous system; stimulates the endocrine glands;
tones the kidneys; and reduces abdominal fat. Helpful in early stages of
enlarged spleen and liver, and diabetes.

BACK
STRETCHING POSE
(Pashchimottanasana)

STRETCHED BOW POSE I
(Akarna Dhanurasana)

Sit with legs stretched forward. Cross right foot over left
foot; grab right big toe with left hand and left big toe
with right hand. Inhale slowly and pull right
foot up to left ear. Hold breath in pose;
then exhale slowly and return to
sitting position. Reverse
legs and repeat. **Benefits**:
Improves circulation and
flexibility; strengthens
shoulders, hips, wrists,
and feet; promotes agility;
and is particularly good
for children.

NOBILITY POSE
(Bhadrasana)

Sit on the floor. Bring soles of feet together, clasp hands around feet, and pull heels in as close to the body as possible. Inhale slowly and press knees down toward floor, keeping spine, neck, and head in a straight line. Hold breath in pose. Concentrate on *ajna chakra*. Exhale slowly and release. *Notes:* In a variation hands are placed on knees, pressing them down gently. The Nobility Pose can be used as a meditation pose, breathing naturally. **Benefits:** Relieves urinary disorders and sciatic pain; keeps the kidneys, prostate, bladder, and ovaries functioning properly; strengthens the reproductive glands and aids in celibacy. Recommended for women, as it helps regulate the menstrual cycle; also recommended during pregnancy.

STRETCHED BOW POSE II
(Akarna Dhanurasana)

Sit with legs stretched forward. Grab left foot (or big toe) with left hand and right big toe with right hand. Inhale slowly and pull left foot up to left ear. Hold breath in pose; then exhale slowly and return to sitting position. Repeat with right leg. **Benefits:** Same as for Stretched Bow Pose I.

43

HALF SPINAL TWIST
(Ardha Matsyendrasana)

Sit with right heel folded alongside left hip. Raise the left knee, cross left foot over folded right leg, and place left foot flat on floor beside right thigh. Bring right upper arm around to the outside of left knee and grab left foot with right hand. Bend left arm behind back, inhale, and twist spine and head to the left, looking back over left shoulder as far as possible. (Straighten spine, neck, and head by stretching torso upward before twisting.) Hold breath in pose; then exhale and untwist slowly. Reverse legs and arms and repeat. **Benefits**: Gives strength, flexibility, and fresh blood supply to the spine; massages abdominal organs, increasing appetite and digestive fire; retards aging; tones the nervous system; and strengthens the reproductive glands.

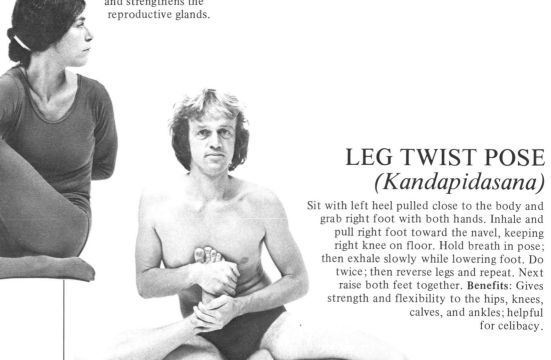

LEG TWIST POSE
(Kandapidasana)

Sit with left heel pulled close to the body and grab right foot with both hands. Inhale and pull right foot toward the navel, keeping right knee on floor. Hold breath in pose; then exhale slowly while lowering foot. Do twice; then reverse legs and repeat. Next raise both feet together. **Benefits**: Gives strength and flexibility to the hips, knees, calves, and ankles; helpful for celibacy.

44

COW'S HEAD POSE
(Gomukhasana)

Sit with right leg folded over left leg so right knee is above left knee. Bring the feet toward the back, resting beside the hips. Raise right arm overhead and bend the elbow so that the hand hangs down behind back. Put left hand behind back and grasp right hand. Inhale slowly and stretch by pulling up with right arm and down with left arm. Hold breath in pose, keeping spine, neck, and head straight. Exhale slowly, reversing legs and arms, and repeat on other side. *Note:* Those who cannot clasp hands may hold a sock in the upper hand and grab the other end of sock with lower hand. **Benefits:** Strengthens the spine, aids in celibacy, helps remove muscular pains in the back and shoulders, cures abdominal weaknesses, and alleviates indigestion and insomnia.

NAVEL-ANUS LOCK
(Uddiyana Mulabandha Asana)

Sit on right heel, folding right leg so the knee rests on the floor. Turn head and torso to face the same direction as the right knee. Stretch left leg back, knee resting on floor. Place right hand on right knee; bend left leg and grab left foot with left hand. Inhale and gently pull left foot toward navel. Hold breath in pose; then exhale slowly, reverse legs, and repeat. **Benefits:** Stretches the thigh muscles, makes the knees flexible, strengthens the reproductive glands, pushes *prana* into *sushumna*, and calms the mind.

45

LOTUS POSE *(Padmasana)*

Sit on the floor with legs crossed. Raise the left foot up onto right thigh, as close to the hip as possible; place right foot on the left thigh, close to left hip. Keep the head, neck, and spine in a straight line; hands rest on knees. This is a meditation pose—breathe naturally. *Note:* Women generally should reverse the legs, placing the left foot on top. **Benefits:** Calms the mind and pushes *prana* into *sushumna.* The position of the crossed legs holds the spine in its natural curve; allows the vital organs to fall into correct position; gives rest to the heart; and makes hips, knees, and ankles flexible.

FREE POSE *(Muktasana)*

Sit on floor and fold legs loosely, one in front of the other. Keep the head, neck, and spine straight, hands on knees. Breathe naturally in this pose for meditation. **Benefits:** Calms the mind and facilitates sitting for a long period of time.

46

ADEPT'S POSE *(Siddhasana)*

Sit with legs crossed. Men should place left heel under testicles and lift the right foot onto left thigh, with right heel resting on the genitals (directly over the left heel). Women should place left heel in front of anus, right heel on top of left. Keep head, neck, and spine in a straight line and breathe naturally. *Note:* This pose is highly recommended for meditation. **Benefits:** Calms the mind, helps in celibacy, and pushes *prana* into *sushumna.*

LAP-LYING POSE *(Svankashayanasana)*

Sit in Lotus Pose. Stretch left arm behind the back and grab left big toe. Place right hand on right side of face. Tucking elbow in toward lap, exhale and bend to the side so that head rests on right knee. Hold breath out in pose; then inhale and sit up. Reverse arms and 'lie down' on the left knee.
Benefits: Intensifies benefits of the Lotus Pose. Aids digestion, increases peristalsis, and relieves constipation.

YOGA MUDRA

Sit in Lotus Pose. Cross arms behind back and grab left big toe with left hand, right big toe with right hand. Or simply grab left wrist with right hand behind the back. Inhale deeply, then exhale and slowly bend forward, resting forehead on floor. Hold breath out in pose; then inhale and sit up. *Note:* When used as a meditation posture, breathe naturally and concentrate on *ajna chakra.* **Benefits:** Intensifies benefits of Lotus Pose. Increases memory and gastric fire; strengthens the spine, waist, lungs, heart, and abdomen.

HIDDEN LOTUS POSE *(Gupta Padmasana)*

Sit in Lotus Pose. Stand on knees, place hands on floor in front, and lie down on stomach with forehead on floor. Place palms together behind the back with fingers pointing toward the head. Breathe slowly and deeply in this pose for one to five minutes. *Note:* Recommended for women; helpful for alleviating menstrual pain. **Benefits:** Strengthens lungs, spine, waist, and reproductive glands.

47

THUNDERBOLT POSE
(Vajrasana)

Kneel and sit on calves, knees together. Place hands on knees, keeping arms and back straight. Either close the eyes, or focus on the tip of the nose. Breathe slowly and deeply. This pose can be used for meditation. *Note:* This is the one *asana* that may be practiced directly after eating. **Benefits**: Calms the mind; aids digestion.

CAT POSE
(Vidalasana)

Kneel on 'all fours', with hands and knees slightly apart. Arms and thighs should be perpendicular to floor. Make the mouth like a pipe and inhale through it with a hissing sound. At the same time, arch the back up like an angry cat and lower head into *jalandhara bandha.* Hold breath in this position. Exhale slowly through the mouth, raising the head and arching the back down toward floor. Repeat several times. **Benefits**: Makes the spine flexible and strong, aids digestion, and strengthens muscles of the back and abdomen. Recommended for women during menstruation or pregnancy.

ON-THE-KNEES SERIES

48

CAMEL POSE
(Ushtrasana)

Sit on the heels, knees slightly apart. Reach back and grab heels with hands. Inhale and push buttocks and abdomen forward, arching back and bending head back. Hold breath in pose; then exhale slowly and return to sitting position. *Note:* Beginners can start by standing on knees; from here inhale slowly and reach back, first with one hand to grab one heel, then with the other hand to grab the other heel. **Benefits:** Expands and develops the chest; strengthens the lungs, spine, and reproductive glands; stimulates digestion; cures constipation; and increases flexibility.

TORTOISE POSE
(Kurmasana)

Kneel and then sit on floor between the feet, spreading knees apart. Exhale and slowly bend forward, touching palms, arms, chin, and chest to the floor. Buttocks remain on floor with arms stretched straight forward. Hold breath out in pose; then inhale and slowly come back up. **Benefits:** Strengthens the liver and kidneys, increases gastric juices, alleviates dysentery and indigestion, and reduces fat.

49

ALLIGATOR POSE
(Makarasana)

Lie face down on floor, arms at sides.
Inhale slowly and raise head, shoulders, and torso,
arching back. Tip head back and look up. Hold
breath in pose; then exhale slowly and come down.
Note: It is helpful if someone else grasps the ankles to
hold the feet down. **Benefits:** Makes the spine flexible; reduces
abdominal fat; strengthens the digestive system;
increases appetite; and strengthens the abdomen, back,
and legs.

FULL
ALLIGATOR
(Purna Makarasana)

Lie face down on floor, arms at sides. Inhale and raise head, shoulders, chest, arms,
and legs off floor. Body balances on the abdomen. Hold breath in pose; then exhale and lower
body back to floor. *Note:* The Full Alligator Pose
is complementary to the Leg-Hand Lifting Pose.
Benefits: Same as for the Alligator Pose.

ON-THE-
STOMACH SERIES 50

BOW POSE *(Dhanurasana)*

Lie face down on floor. Bend knees, reach back and grab ankles with hands. Inhale and lift head, chest, and thighs off floor as high as possible, stretching the body into a bow shape. Tip head back. Hold breath in pose; then exhale slowly releasing legs and coming down. *Note:* The Bow Pose is complementary to the Plow Pose. **Benefits:** Strengthens the spine, intestines, liver, and kidneys; aids digestion; reduces fat; and makes the body flexible.

COBRA POSE *(Bhujangasana)*

Lie face down on the floor. Place palms on floor beside shoulders. Inhale and slowly raise head and chest off floor, arching the neck backwards. Look up and back. Hold breath in pose; then exhale and come down slowly. *Note:* The Cobra Pose is complementary to the Back Stretching Pose. **Benefits:** Makes the spine flexible; relieves gastro-intestinal disorders; expands the chest, thereby strengthening the lungs and heart; awakens *kundalini;* and is recommended for women after childbirth because it strengthens the reproductive organs.

HALF LOCUST *(Ardha Shalabhasana)*

Lie face down on floor, arms at sides and forehead (or chin) touching floor. Place hands under thighs, with palms down or by making fists. Inhale and raise both legs as high as possible, keeping forehead (or chin) on floor. Hold breath in pose; then exhale slowly while lowering legs. *Notes:* Beginners can raise one leg at a time first; then try raising both legs together. The Half Locust Pose is complementary to the Leg Lifting Pose. **Benefits:** Strengthens the abdomen, legs, back, neck, spine, heart, and lungs; tones the ovaries and uterus; relieves menstrual pain; and reduces fat.

51

DUCK POSE *(Vakasana)*

Squat down on toes, knees apart. Place hands on floor between legs, upper arms against inside of knees. While inhaling slowly, bend elbows and lean forward. Then raise the body and legs off the floor, resting knees on the upper arms. Draw heels up close to the buttocks. Hold breath with *mula bandha* while balancing; then exhale slowly coming down. **Benefits:** Strengthens the reproductive glands, the semen, and the abdominal organs; improves digestion; and strengthens the spine, shoulders, and arms.

TOE BALANCE POSE *(Padangushthasana)*

Crouch down, balancing on the toes. Sit on right heel, raising left foot to place it on top of right thigh. Place palms together in front of chest, fingers pointing upward. Fix the gaze on the tip of the nose. Inhale and hold breath while balancing in this pose; then exhale, switch legs, and repeat. **Benefits:** Tones the reproductive glands; aids in celibacy; strengthens the mind; increases memory; and strengthens the ankles, legs, and spine.

EIGHT CURVE POSE *(Ashta Vakrasana)*

Sit on left hip with legs bent, right on top of left, and lock the left foot over the right foot. Slip right hand between bent knees and place it palm down on floor. Put left palm on floor under left shoulder. Inhale and tilt the body forward, bending elbows and lifting hips and legs off the floor. (Right leg can rest on right upper arm.) Hold breath and balance; then exhale slowly, reverse legs and arms, and repeat. **Benefits:** Increases overall strength, develops muscles of abdomen and arms, strengthens the nervous system, and slows the aging process.

PEACOCK POSE
(Mayurasana)

Taking the position for the Swan Pose, inhale and bring head off floor by shifting the body slightly toward feet. Then raise legs by shifting body forward again. Hold breath while balancing on the hands; then exhale slowly lowering head and feet. Either return to kneeling position or relax in the Reverse Relaxation Pose. **Benefits**: Increases digestive fire, alleviating indigestion and constipation; is helpful for diabetes, hemorrhoids, and inflammation of the intestines or liver; stimulates circulation of blood in the abdomen; tones the lungs; rouses *kundalini;* and strengthens the wrists, arms, and abdominal muscles.

SWAN POSE
(Hamsasana)

Kneel on the floor with knees apart. Put hands on floor between knees, with palms down and fingers pointing toward feet. Put the elbows as close together as possible, lean forward a little, and press them into the stomach. Inhale and put the forehead on the floor and extend the legs straight back, toes on floor. Holding breath in pose, slowly raise one leg, pause, lower it, and raise the other leg in the same way. Do this several times; then slowly exhale and return to starting position. *Note:* This is the first stage of the Peacock Pose. It can be practiced by beginners or by those unable to do the full Peacock Pose. **Benefits**: Same as for Peacock Pose.

53

HEADSTAND *(Shirshasana)*

Using a mat for protection, kneel and place forearms on floor in front of knees. Touch right hand to left elbow; this measures the proper distance between elbows for a steady base for the Headstand. Without moving elbows from this position, clasp hands together to form a tripod. Raise hips and put head on floor between clasped hands. Weight rests either on forehead, on center top of head, or on back top of head. Now lift knees off the floor and raise the hips by walking toward the head. When the back is vertical, slowly lift feet off floor, bring knees in to chest, and balance with knees bent until steady. Then slowly raise feet up until legs are straight. Breathe naturally in this pose. *Notes:* Beginners may use a wall or the corner of a room for support. After doing the Headstand for five to ten minutes, do the Baby Pose for one or two minutes, then the Palm Tree Pose for two to three minutes, then the Relaxation Pose for up to five minutes.
Benefits: Improves memory, eyesight, and hearing; opens the *nadis;* allows one to hear inner sounds *(nada);* and awakens *kundalini.* Strengthens digestive and reproductive organs; purifies the semen; and is helpful in the treatment of sterility, diabetes, piles, and asthma.

BABY POSE
(Balakasana)

Sit on heels with arms at sides. Inhale deeply, then exhale and lean forward, touching forehead to the floor. Arms stretch back toward feet, palms upward. Breathe naturally in pose; then inhale gently while coming up. *Note:* The Baby Pose is complementary to all backward-bending poses. **Benefits**: Increases memory, strengthens eyesight, and facilitates blood circulation.

RABBIT POSE
(Shashangasana)

Sit on the heels as in the Thunderbolt Pose. Grab ankles with hands and bend head down to floor, tucking the chin well into the neck. Inhale and raise the hips up so the lower legs and thighs make a right angle. The body weight rests either on forehead, on center top of head, or on back top of head. Hold breath in pose; then exhale while lowering hips and raising head back to the Thunderbolt Pose. *Note:* The Rabbit Pose is an alternate pose for those who cannot do the Headstand. **Benefits**: Same as for Headstand.

HEADSTAND SERIES 54

RELAXATION POSE
(Shavasana)

Lie flat on the back like a corpse, arms at sides and head rolled slightly to one side. Close eyes and relax, breathing naturally. The mind should be thoughtless. *Note:* Practice the Relaxation Pose after each series, or after several strenuous poses, for fifteen to twenty seconds. At the end of *asana* practice, do this pose for five to ten minutes. It is also practiced after *pranayama* and meditation. **Benefits:** Facilitates blood circulation, relieves fatigue, and reduces stress and depression.

REVERSE RELAXATION POSE
(Advasana)

Lie down on the stomach with arms at sides and head to one side. Close eyes and relax, breathing naturally. *Note:* This pose is practiced after every three or four *asanas* done on the stomach. **Benefits:** Same as for the Relaxation Pose.

ARATI
Worship by Light

*"In devotional path
there is no end.
There is always a craving
for God.
The more you get
the more you want to get
until you dissolve into
God's love."*

ARATI IS A DEVOTIONAL SERVICE offered to one's chosen form of God. The service is performed at sunrise and sunset; it also concludes *puja* (worship). Any number of people may participate. The officiant, *pujari*, must bathe and put on clean, white clothes before the ceremony. White symbolizes purity; ideally the clothes are kept for *arati* alone.

During the ceremony a light is waved around the deity in a figure *Om* (ॐ). The light symbolizes knowledge, which the deity possesses. A bell is rung throughout *arati;* its sound represents *nada.* Water, a symbol of divine nectar, is offered to wash the deity's feet; it is also offered to the deity to drink. At the end a song honoring the chosen deity is sung.

Preparation

The *puja* table should be against a north or east wall. Traditionally it has three levels. The lowest level is the floor, where the *pujari* stands; on the middle level the *arati* equipage is placed; the highest level is for the main image of one's chosen deity.

Decorate the table with flowers, candles, and pictures of saints. Put one wick in each cup of an *arati* lamp and place it in the center on the middle level. (Wicks are made from twisted cotton and dipped in clarified butter or sesame oil.) Lacking an *arati* lamp, one may put wicks on a small metal plate or use a candle.

Put a square of red cloth under the main deity on the upper level. Fold another piece of cloth and place it to the right of the *arati* lamp.

Also on the right side of the lamp keep three incense sticks, three small vessels—two filled with water and the third one empty, and a food offering (*prasad*—this is usually sweets, nuts, or small pieces of fruit).

To the left of the *arati* lamp place a bell with a long handle. The *pujari* rings this bell throughout the ceremony. Participants may clap or use musical instruments—drums, conch, cymbals, etc.

The Ceremony

Stand to the left of the *puja* table so all participants can see the deity.

Light candles and incense. Move *arati* lamp to the left. Dip the ring finger in water and make a five-pointed star in the middle of the table; the star represents the five elements. Inside the star make a dot *(bindu)* to symbolize the center of energy. Replace the lamp over the star.

Moving clockwise, light the wicks of the *arati* lamp with a piece of incense or a match. Pick up the first water vessel and circle it clockwise over the lamp; then pour a little water from it into the empty container. This symbolically purifies the lamp and the altar.

Display *matsyah*, *yoni*, and *nirvanam* hand *mudras* to the deity.

Now everyone stands.

Pick up the bell in the left hand and then the *arati* lamp in the right hand. Ring the bell while gracefully waving

"For attaining God we have to push ourselves to worship, meditate, and pray. In that pushing our mind gets purified and we lose our ego. When the ego is reduced, then God also starts pulling."

*"Contentment,
compassion, and tolerance
are the pillars
of peace."*

the lamp. Participants beat drums, play cymbals, clap, etc. There are many methods of waving the lamp; one may create one's own pattern, or use the following.

Making *Om* signs (ॐ) with the lamp, wave it in front of each image on the alter. Make a clockwise circle with the lamp, honoring all deities in the universe, and then raise it high above the head of the main deity. Make the *Om* sign three times coming down from the head to the feet. Then wave the lamp three times at the deity's feet, three at the heart, and three at the forehead. Circle the bell around the *arati* lamp and put the lamp down.

While still ringing the bell, pick up the first water vessel, hold it up to the deity's feet, and then pour a bit of water into the third container. Repeat this two more times, and set the vessel down on the left side of the *puja* table. This symbolizes washing the deity's feet. Pick up the folded cloth with the right hand and pass it three times in front of the deity's feet, symbolically drying them.

Put the cloth down, pick up the lamp and wave it as before. Again circle the bell around the lamp and set the lamp down.

Using the second water vessel, offer water to the deity's mouth in the same way as for the feet, except place the vessel back down on the right side of the table when finished. Symbolically, you are offering the deity a drink of water. Then pass the cloth in front of

the deity's mouth.

Again lift the lamp and offer it to the four main directions. Begin with one wave in front of you, turn 90° clockwise and wave it to your right, turn further to the right and wave it to the back, then bring the lamp back past the front and wave it to your left. Now put both the lamp and the bell down. Participants stop playing instruments at this time.

Take the second water vessel again and pour a little water in the right palm. Carry the water clockwise around the lamp and then pour it over the bell. Pour some more water into the hand and toss it over the right shoulder; pour again and throw over left shoulder, and again straight back over the head. Then place the vessel down on left side of table. This act symbolizes the blessing of God to everyone; water also purifies and washes away one's sins.

Pick up the bell and lamp again and offer the light to everyone, beginning on your right and making a full circle clockwise. Participants may hold their hands toward the flame and then bow to the deity.

A song honoring the chosen deity is sung. There are many *arati* songs—the one given here is dedicated to the universal God. One may sing any song in praise of God. The food offering is now served to everyone present. All of the food, which has been consecrated by the ceremony, should be eaten.

Allow the wicks in the *arati* lamp to burn out by themselves.

ARATI SONG

Om Jaya Jagadīsh Hare
Prabhu Jaya Jagadīsh Hare
Bhakta Janŏ Ke Saṅkaṭ
Bhakta Janŏ Ke Saṅkaṭ
Chhin Mĕ Dūr Kare
Om Jaya Jagadīsh Hare

Jo Dhyāve Phal Pāve
Dukh Vinashe Mankā
Swāmī Dukh Vinashe Mankā
Sukh Sampati Ghar Ā-ve (2)
Kashṭa Miṭe Tan Kā
Om Jaya Jagadīsh Hare

Māta Pitā Tum Mere
Sharaṇ Gahŭ Kis Kī
Swāmī Sharaṇ Gahŭ Kis Kī
Tum Bin Aur Na Dūjā (2)
Āsa Karŭ Jis Kī
Om Jaya Jagadīsh Hare

Tum Pūraṇ Paramātmā
Tum Aṅtar Yāmi
Swāmī Tum Aṅtar Yāmi
Pārabrahma Parameshwara (2)
Tum Sab Ke Swāmī
Om Jaya Jagadīsh Hare

Tum Karuṇā Ke Sāgar
Tum Pālan Kartā
Swāmī Tum Pālan Kartā
Mǎi Sevak Tum Swāmī (2)
Kṛipā Karo Bharatā
Om Jaya Jagadīsh Hare

Tum Ho Ek Agochar
Sabake Prāṇ Patī
Swāmī Sabake Prāṇ Patī
Kis Bidhi Milŭ Dayā Maya (2)
Tum Ko Mǎi Kumatī
Om Jaya Jagadīsh Hare

Dīn Bandhu Dukh Hartā
Tum Rakshak Mere
Swāmī Tum Rakshak Mere
Apane Hāth Uṭhā-o (2)
Dvār Pārā Tere
Om Jaya Jagadīsh Hare

Vishaya Vikār Miṭā-o
Pāp Haro Devā
Swāmī Pāp Haro Devā
Shraddhā Bhakti Barhā-o (2)
Santan Kī Sevā
Om Jaya Jagadīsh Hare

Om, glory to the Lord of the universe
O Lord, glory to the Lord of the universe
Who removes the miseries of his devotees in a moment.
Om, glory to the Lord of the universe.

One who meditates on the Lord attains the fruits of
Contemplation, & sorrows are removed from the mind.
O Lord, sorrows are removed from the mind.
May happiness and wealth come to the house
And physical pains be removed.
Om, glory to the Lord of the universe.

You are my mother and father;
In whom else can I take refuge?
O Lord, in whom else can I take refuge?
There is no one else besides You
In whom I could put my hope.
Om, glory to the Lord of the universe.

You are the perfect Supreme Lord—
Knower of all hearts.
O Lord, knower of all hearts.
Supreme Creator, Supreme Lord—
You are the master of all
Om, glory to the Lord of the universe.

You are an ocean of compassion,
You are the nourisher.
O Lord, You are the nourisher.
I am the servant and You are my master;
O Lord, have mercy on me.
Om, glory to the Lord of the universe.

You are beyond the mind and the senses—
Lord of everyone's life.
O Lord, Lord of everyone's life.
O All-Gracious, how can I, so evil-minded, find You?
Om, glory to the Lord of the universe.

Friend of the poor, remover of pain—
You are my protector.
O Lord, You are my protector.
Extend Your hand—I am lying at Your door.
Om, glory to the Lord of the universe.

Erase sensual desires, remove all sins.
O Lord, remove all sins.
Increase faith and devotion—
May we serve the saints.
Om, glory to the Lord of the universe.

HAND MUDRAS

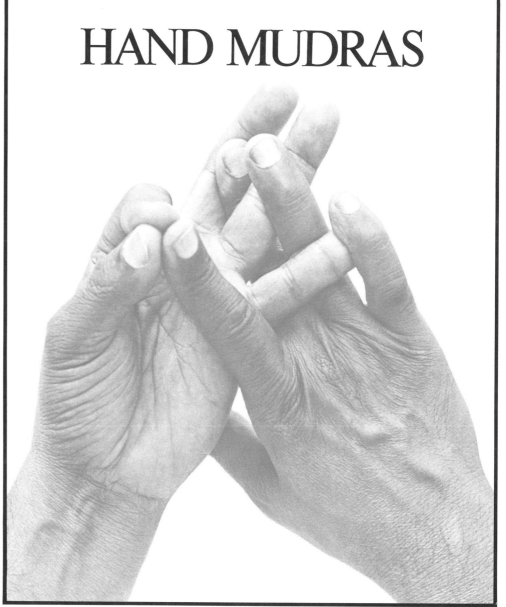

*"Prayer
from a pure
heart is the
most powerful energy.
By your prayers
you can attain
peace."*

Raghunath Rodney Polden

HAND *MUDRAS* ARE A SERIES OF symbolic gestures. They depict the evolution of the universe and the eventual involution of individual consciousness back to its divine source. The essence of hand *mudras* is devotion, as each *mudra* is an offering, a gift to the Divine. The hands perform a graceful worship, flowing rhythmically with a slow and steady pattern of breathing. A cycle of twenty-four movements is offered in preparation for meditation, while another cycle of eight follows meditation.

BEFORE MEDITATION

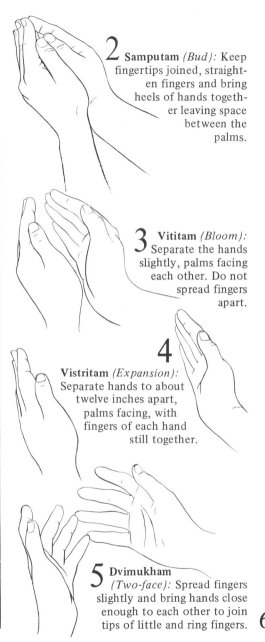

1 **Sumukham** *(Faces):* With hands in front of chest, close to the heart, join fingertips of both hands. The nails of the fingers face outward and the thumbnails face inward.

2 **Samputam** *(Bud):* Keep fingertips joined, straighten fingers and bring heels of hands together leaving space between the palms.

3 **Vititam** *(Bloom):* Separate the hands slightly, palms facing each other. Do not spread fingers apart.

4 **Vistritam** *(Expansion):* Separate hands to about twelve inches apart, palms facing, with fingers of each hand still together.

5 **Dvimukham** *(Two-face):* Spread fingers slightly and bring hands close enough to each other to join tips of little and ring fingers.

"Faith, devotion, and right aim—these three things are the main guides for the spiritual journey."

61

*"No one can please everyone.
Your mental peace
is more important. If
you are in peace
then others around you
will feel peace.
So your best
effort should be to
work on yourself."*

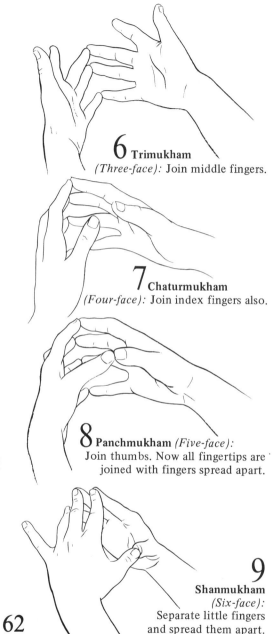

6 Trimukham
(Three-face): Join middle fingers.

7 Chaturmukham
(Four-face): Join index fingers also.

8 Panchmukham *(Five-face):*
Join thumbs. Now all fingertips are
joined with fingers spread apart.

9
Shanmukham
(Six-face):
Separate little fingers
and spread them apart.

62

10 Adhomukham
(Down Face):

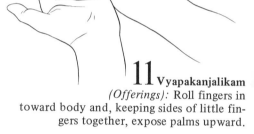

Close
fingers
and invert
hands so that
backs of fingers touch, pointing
straight down. Thumbs are separated.

11 Vyapakanjalikam
(Offerings): Roll fingers in
toward body and, keeping sides of little fingers together, expose palms upward.

12
Shakatam *(Cart):* Turn
hands over and join tips of
thumbs. Curl middle, ring, and
little fingers in toward palms and
leave index fingers straight, pointing slightly
inward but not touching.

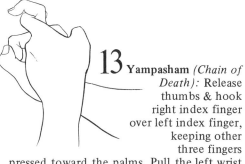

13 **Yampasham** *(Chain of Death):* Release thumbs & hook right index finger over left index finger, keeping other three fingers pressed toward the palms. Pull the left wrist toward the chest while pushing right wrist down and away from the body.

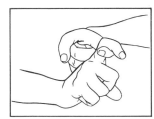

13. *Front view*

14 **Granthitam** *(Knot of Maya):* Clasp hands together, fingers crossed, with left index finger in front of right index finger.

14. *Front view*

15 **Unmukhonmukham** *(Up and Down Face):* Bunch fingertips of each hand close together. Touch the tips of the left hand, fingers pointing downward, with the tips of the right hand, fingers pointing upward. Then, with fingertips still touching, switch so the right hand is on top.

16 **Pralambam** *(Spread Offerings):* With thumbtips together, spread hands forward so palms face down. Fingers are straight, not spread apart.

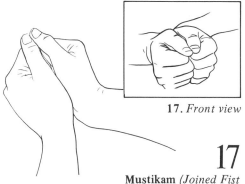

17. *Front view*

17 **Mustikam** *(Joined Fist Offering):* Curl fingers in toward palms and bring fists together with thumbs side by side.

"Attachment to God is devotion."

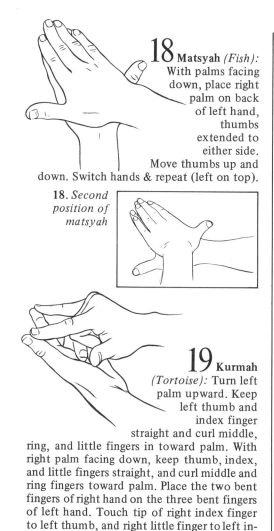

18 Matsyah *(Fish):* With palms facing down, place right palm on back of left hand, thumbs extended to either side. Move thumbs up and down. Switch hands & repeat (left on top).

18. Second position of matsyah

19 Kurmah *(Tortoise):* Turn left palm upward. Keep left thumb and index finger straight and curl middle, ring, and little fingers in toward palm. With right palm facing down, keep thumb, index, and little fingers straight, and curl middle and ring fingers toward palm. Place the two bent fingers of right hand on the three bent fingers of left hand. Touch tip of right index finger to left thumb, and right little finger to left index. Right thumb does not touch other hand.

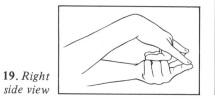

19. Right side view

20 Varahkam *(Boar):* Keep right index finger touching left thumb and grab three fingers of right hand (middle, ring, little) with four fingers of left hand. Right thumb rests between left thumb and right index finger, and all three point upward.

20. Front view

21 Simhakrantam *(Of Lion Nature):* Open hands and place them beside shoulders with palms facing forward.

Mudras 18, 19, 20, and 21 represent various forms that Vishnu assumed to help the Earth. The Lion form symbolizes courage.

"It's not entirely the method that brings enlightenment. It is faith, devotion, and dispassion that make a method effective."

64

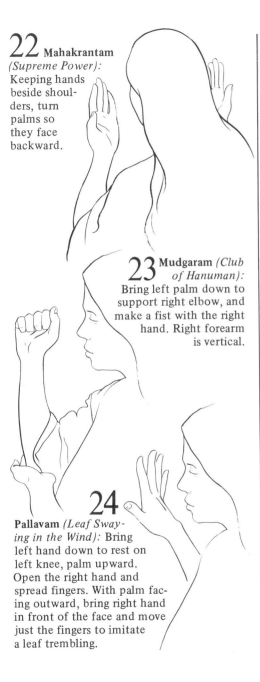

22 **Mahakrantam**
(Supreme Power):
Keeping hands
beside shoul-
ders, turn
palms so
they face
backward.

23 **Mudgaram** *(Club*
of Hanuman):
Bring left palm down to
support right elbow, and
make a fist with the right
hand. Right forearm
is vertical.

24

Pallavam *(Leaf Sway-*
ing in the Wind): Bring
left hand down to rest on
left knee, palm upward.
Open the right hand and
spread fingers. With palm facing outward, bring right hand
in front of the face and move
just the fingers to imitate
a leaf trembling.

AFTER MEDITATION

The eight hand *mudras* that are performed after meditation are like salu-
tations to God, or prayers. These slow,
graceful movements provide a helpful
transition from meditation to outer
awareness.

I **Surabhi** *(Cow):* Place
palms together in front
of chest. Cross left
middle finger
behind right
middle finger, and
left ring finger
behind right ring
finger. Spread index fingers
apart and join left index finger to right middle finger, right
index finger to left middle fin-
ger. Spread little fingers apart and join left
little finger to right ring finger, right little finger to left ring finger. Thumbs stay side by
side, and all fingers point upward.

"Sadhana
makes a ladder to
attain peace.
Every day's sadhana *makes*
one step of the ladder.
If we miss one day.
we lose one step."

65

*"Path of devotion
is the best.
By surrendering to God,
by chanting God's name
and glory,
and by meditating
on God's form,
one can row one's boat
in the ocean of
the world without
getting hit
by the mighty waves
of desires,
attachment,
and ego."*

II **Jnanam** *(Knowledge):* Join index fingers to thumbs, keeping other three fingers of each hand straight. (This position of the fingers is called *jnana mudra.*) Place right hand, palm facing forward, on the heart with the three straight fingers pointing upward. Place left hand, palm upward, on the left knee.

III **Vairagyam** *(Dispassion):* Keeping hands in *jnana mudra,* place right hand, palm upward, on right knee.

IV **Yoni** *(Female Sex Organ):* Place palms together in front of chest. Cross right ring finger behind left ring finger (4—a). Separate index fingers and hook right index finger around tip of left ring finger, left index finger around tip of right ring finger (4—b). Cross right little finger behind left little finger (4—c). Place thumbs side by side at the base of middle fingers, which are kept straight.

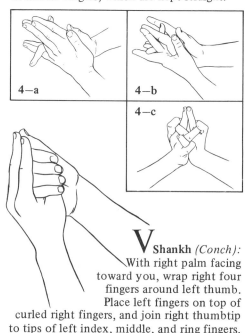

V **Shankh** *(Conch):* With right palm facing toward you, wrap right four fingers around left thumb. Place left fingers on top of curled right fingers, and join right thumbtip to tips of left index, middle, and ring fingers.

66

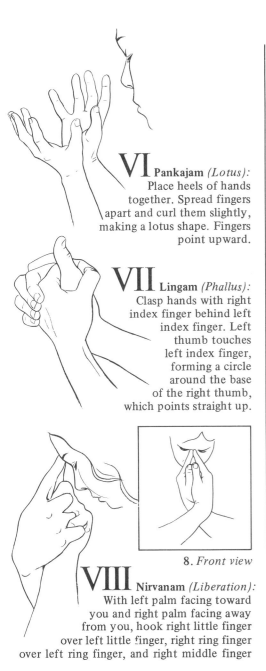

VI **Pankajam** *(Lotus):*
Place heels of hands together. Spread fingers apart and curl them slightly, making a lotus shape. Fingers point upward.

VII **Lingam** *(Phallus):*
Clasp hands with right index finger behind left index finger. Left thumb touches left index finger, forming a circle around the base of the right thumb, which points straight up.

8. Front view

VIII **Nirvanam** *(Liberation):*
With left palm facing toward you and right palm facing away from you, hook right little finger over left little finger, right ring finger over left ring finger, and right middle finger

over left middle finger (8—a). Keeping fingers locked with index fingers straight, turn left hand over clockwise and turn right hand slightly counter-clockwise until palms meet. Wrists are crossed, tips of index fingers touch, and thumbs are side by side (8—b). Now bring index fingers down, in toward the body, and up to touch the eyebrow center (above). This last position of the hands is named *nirvana* (liberation).

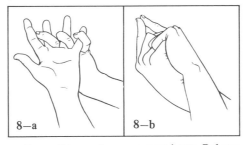

8—a   8—b

From this *mudra*, one may bow: Release hands, keeping arms crossed at wrists. Place fingers in *jnana mudra* (8—c). Uncross the arms by sweeping the hands in graceful opposing circles. With palms facing upward, hands side by side, bow the head, bringing forehead down to the heels of the hands (below).

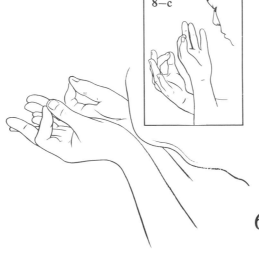

8—c

"Love everyone including yourself. This is real sadhana."

"The main thing is selfless service. It sounds easy but it is very hard. Our mind is so selfish that in anything we do it always seeks for its own benefit."

APPENDICES

SCHEDULE *for* DAILY SADHANA

Sadhana should be practiced daily and systematically. It is better to start with a few practices and build gradually. Pranayama is chosen according to one's capability.

Beginning (First Three Months)

Shat Karma
Jala Neti and Sutra Neti (daily)
Danta Dhauti (daily)
Vamana Dhauti (once a week)
Jala Vasti (once a week)
Trataka on candle flame (daily)
Nauli (daily)

Four Purifications
Nadishodhana (10 rounds)
Kapala Bhati (3 rounds)
Agnisara Dhauti (3 rounds)
Ashvini Mudra (3 rounds)

Tri Bandha
Mula Bandha (10 rounds)
Jalandhara Bandha (10 rounds)
Uddiyana Bandha (10 rounds)

Pranayama
Tribandha (10 rounds)
Dirgha Rechak (10 rounds)
Dirgha Purak (10 rounds)
Ujjayi (10 rounds)
Shitali or Sitkari (10 rounds)
Bhramari (5 rounds)

Mudras
Maha Mudra (2 on each side)

Dharana & Dhyana
Japa of Om (5 minutes)
Hand Mudras (24 Before Meditation)
Prayers, Eight Kriyas
Meditation (20 minutes)
Hand Mudras (8 After Meditation)

Asana as per ability, without retention

Intermediate (After Three Months)

Shat Karma (add to previous)
Vastra Dhauti (once a week)
Varisara Dhauti (once a month)

Four Purifications
Nadi Shodhana (40 rounds)
Kapala Bhati (10 rounds)
Agnisara Dhauti (10 rounds)
Ashvini Mudra (10 rounds)

Note: *As an alternative to doing the Four Purifications separately, one may do the intermediate (combined) method, starting with 5 rounds and increasing gradually to 20 rounds.*

Pranayama (Choose any combination; maximum 40 rounds)
Ujjayi
Shitali or Sitkari
Bhramari
Bhastrika (3 rounds)
Sahita Kumbhaka (5–15 rounds)

Mudras
Maha Mudra (2–10 on each side)
Maha Bandha (2–10 on each side)
Maha Vedha Mudra (2–10 times)
Shaktichalana Mudra (3–10 times)

Dharana & Dhyana
Japa of Om (10 minutes)
Hand Mudras (24 Before Meditation)
Prayers, Eight Kriyas
Meditation (45 minutes)
Hand Mudras (8 After Meditation)

Asana as per ability, with retention

"Whether you set a goal or not, if you practice sadhana regularly its result will be peace."

69

SADHANA DURING PREGNANCY

photo by
Christopher
Wentworth

*"A baby
feels protected
in the mother's lap
the same way
a yogi
feels protected
in the lap of God."*

Changes in hormone levels are responsible for some of the side effects of pregnancy, such as nausea, headaches, constipation, fatigue, consciousness changes, and frequent or intense dreams.

Proper diet, sleep, and exercise are essential for the mother-to-be. She should eat light, nourishing food and avoid alcohol, nicotine, and caffeine. Desires for certain foods should be satisfied as far as possible, rather than suppressed. Eight hours of sleep are recommended. Light exercise, such as daily walks in fresh air, assists circulation of blood in both the mother and the baby. It is also important for a pregnant woman to make a conscious effort to sit, stand, and walk with a straight spine.

Most important of all, try to be calm, happy, and peaceful during pregnancy. Enjoy God's creation, study scriptures, meditate, and spend time alone. (Too many social activities can create emotional strain.) This attitude will create positive *samskaras* (impressions, tendencies) in the baby you are carrying.

Shat Karma
    Jala Neti (daily)
    Sutra Neti (once a week)
    Danta Dhauti (daily)
    Trataka on candle flame (daily)

Four Purifications
    Nadishodhana
    Kapala Bhati
    Agnisara Dhauti
        (stop after 3rd month)
    Ashvini Mudra

Pranayama
    Ujjayi
    Shitali or Sitkari
    Bhramari

Mudras
    Maha Mudra (stop after 3rd month)

Dharana & Dhyana
    Continue as usual

70

"There is an unspoken language. It comes from the silence and can't be heard by the ears, only by the heart."

Twenty-two days after childbirth, easy *asanas* can be started. Then slowly add postures until three months after delivery, when all *asanas* may be resumed.

*"For love
and compassion,
how much
time
do you need?"*

Other books by Baba Hari Dass:

Cat & Sparrow
A Child's Garden of Yoga
Essays 1—Binding Thoughts & Liberation
Essays 2—Mind is Our World
Essays 3—Selfless Service: The Spirit of Karma Yoga
Fire Without Fuel
Fun With Fitness Asanas
Hariakhan Baba—Known, Unknown
The Magic Gem—A Story-Coloring Book
Mystic Monkey
Silence Speaks—from the Chalkboard of Baba Hari Dass
Sweeper to Saint—Stories of Holy India
The Yellow Book (out of print)

Tapes/CDs by Sri Rama Publishing:

Anjali—Melodies of Ancient India
Guru Purnima Songs
Horizons—Improvisations for Harp and Flute
Inner Light—Improvisations on East Indian Melodies
Jai Ma Kirtan—Songs to the Divine Mother
Jai Shiva! Kirtan for Shivaratri
Murali Krishna
Radhe Krishna
Songs of the Ramayana
Sri Ram Kirtan—Volumes I & II
Tender Mercies—Hanuman Fellowship Women's Choir

For free catalog of books/tapes/CDs/songbooks please write:
Sri Rama Publishing · Box 2550 · Santa Cruz · California 95063

GLOSSARY

abhyāsah . . . . persistent practice

ahimsā . . . . nonviolence

ajapā . . . . .automatic repetition

ājnā . . . . chakra located between
the eyebrows

anāhata . . .chakra located at the heart

apāna vāyu . . . . vital air between
navel and feet

aparigraha . . . . non-possessiveness

āratī . . . . worship by light

āsana . . . . .posture, seat

ashtanga . . . . eight-limbed

asteya . . . . non-stealing

bandha . . . . .body lock

bhakti . . . . .devotion

bindu . . . . .center

brahmacharya . . . . continence

Brahmarandhra . . . lit. "hole of God",
another name for mula

chakra . . . . .subtle energy center

dhāranā . . . . .concentration

dhauti . . . . internal washing

dhyāna . . . . meditation

granthi . . . . .knot

idā nādi . . . subtle energy channel that
exits through the left nostril

Īshwarapranidhāna . surrender to God

jala . . . . water

japa . . . . mental repetition

kaivalya . . . . liberation

kīrtana . . . . songs, chanting

kriyā . . . . . .activity, practice, method

kumbhaka . . . . .breath retention

kundalinī . . . liberating energy located
at the base of the spine

mālā . . . . string of 108 beads for japa

manipūra . . . . chakra located at
the navel

mantra . . . . . .sacred syllable or words,
sound vibration

mastaka granthi . . . . . ."head knot" at
the base of the skull

mudrā . . . .pose or gesture for stillness
and awakening kundalini

mūla . . . . . . "root"; upper side of the
bindu of sahasrara chakra

mūlādhāra . . . . . chakra located at the
base of the spine

nāda . . . . .subtle sound

nādī . . . . .subtle energy channel
through which prana flows

nauli . . . . intestinal wash

neti . . . . nasal cleaning

niyama . . . . observances

nyāsa . . . . placing divine energy
onto the body

ojas . . . . electrical energy

Om (or Aum) . . . . . primordial sound

pingalā nādī . . . .subtle energy channel
that exits through the right nostril

prāna . . . . .vital energy

prāna vāyu . . . . vital air between
throat and navel

pranāyāma . .control of breath, prana

prasād . . . . . . .food offered to a deity

pratyāhāra . . . . . . withdrawal of mind
from the senses

pūjā . . . . worship

pujārī . . . .one who conducts worship

sādhanā . . . . .spiritual practice

sahasrāra . . . . chakra that fills the
crown of the head

samādhi . . . . states of superconsciousness, trance

samāna vāyu . . . . . . .vital air between
navel and heart

samskāra . . . . . . tendency, impression

santosha . . . . .contentment

satsang . . . . . . .fellowship with truth,
company of good people

satya . . . . truthfulness

shakti . . . . .creative energy

shat karma . six purificatory methods

shaucha . . . . .purity, cleanliness

shodashādhāra . . . . . . sixteen energy
centers for concentration

shrī . . . . . . .underside of the bindu of
sahasrara chakra

sushumnā . . . . . . main nadi located in
center of spine, through
which *kundalini* flows

sūtra . . . . verse, aphorism, string

svādhyāya . . . . scriptural study

svādhishthāna . . . . . chakra located at
the level of the genitals

svayambhu lingam . . . . . .resting place
of kundalini

tapas . . . . .austerity

trātaka . . . . . .gazing, forehead wash

udāna vāyu . . . . .vital air between
throat and top of head

vasti . . . . .enema

vayu . . . . . . vital air, manifestation of
prana in the subtle body

vishuddha . . . . chakra located at
the throat

vritti . . . . thought wave

vyāna vayu . . . . . vital air throughout
the body

yama . . . . restraints

yoga . . . . union

*"Work honestly,
meditate
every day, meet
people
without fear,
and play."*

MOUNT MADONNA CENTER,

sister organization to Sri Rama Publishing, is a spiritual community and seminar facility inspired by Baba Hari Dass and sponsored by the Hanuman Fellowship—a group whose talents and interests are unified by the common practice of Ashtanga Yoga. The Center offers programs throughout the year, including Ashtanga Yoga Teacher Training courses and several four-day Yoga retreats. Located on 355 mountaintop acres of redwood forest and grassland overlooking Monterey Bay, the Center provides a supportive community atmosphere for relaxation, reflection, and a wide variety of learning experiences. Program participants are invited to join in all ongoing activities— celebration, work, and play. For information or brochure write: Mt. Madonna Center, 445 Summit Rd., Watsonville, CA 95076. **SALT SPRING CENTRE:** Another of our related communities, located on Salt Spring Island off Canada's beautiful west coast, offers a wide variety of programs, including in-depth Yoga retreats, self-improvement workshops, women's weekends, and healing seminars. For more information write: Salt Spring Centre, P.O. Box 1133, Ganges, B.C., Canada V0S 1E0. **ASHTANGA YOGA FELLOWSHIP:** Annual Ashtanga Yoga retreats with Baba Hari Dass, on-going Ashtanga Yoga classes, and weekly gatherings for inspirational study and devotional music *(satsang)* are held in Toronto, Canada. For more information please write: Ashtanga Yoga Fellowship, c/o Shakti, The 2nd Concession, RR3, Stouffville, Ontario, Canada L4A 7X4.

AUTHOR Baba Hari Dass receives no money from the sale of his books; his publications are dedicated instead to the needy and homeless children of India. In 1984, in a small village near the Himalayan foothills, he founded Shri Ram Orphanage, with the hope of providing at least some of India's homeless children with a better life. At first there were only two children, but within a year thirteen had come; then the earthquake in 1991 brought nineteen more, and we suddenly became a very large family. We started our own school, built a larger kitchen, and added another two-storey wing onto our first building to accommodate the growing needs. The children of the Orphanage, several of whom came to us as infants with otherwise little chance to live, are now happy and healthy, laughing and running around in our new School playground. With the support and help of many friends and donors, we feel fortunate to be able to make this small but significant difference. For more information about the Orphanage project please feel free to write to us.

Shri Ram Orphanage